Nc

Conor Nolan

Copyright © 2020 by Conor Nolan

All rights reserved. No part of this publication may be reproduced, stored in any form of retrieval system or transmitted in any form or by any means without prior permission in writing from the publishers except for the use of brief quotations in a book review.

Contents

Acknowledgements

To Colm and Michelle
To Miriam and Deniese
To Kyle and Jordan
To Tiernan, Ciaran, Avril and Olivia
And to family, they know who they are

My father always told me that experience is the best teacher.

I am not a psychologist,

I am in no way qualified to speak to you about mental health, or the way we deal with the life we have been given.

But between the ages of ten and twenty, I learned a series of lessons about life.

Here are those lessons.

I hope you enjoy.

1

Nights Like These

I once read that the two most important days of your life are the day that you're born, and the day that you find out why. I've also been told on several occasions that life starts at twenty. For me, those two statements lined up perfectly.

As I sat in a friend's back garden on a July evening in a housing estate in Galway, I was reminded of my good fortune, surrounded by a group that meant the world to me. It's amazing the variety of people you come across in life. A lot of those around me had only stumbled across my path in recent months. I had started a new job and had formed that unbreakable bond you seem to form with your workmates. Everyone knows everything, and there aren't really any secrets.

Luke, one of these new colleagues, was turning twenty and had organised a house party. There were around fifteen of us there, and after about an hour, I was my usual, animated, drunk self. My wise and wonderful alter ego, 'Drunk Conor', as I call him, has a tendency to light up the room in a way that 'Sober Conor' can only envy. A few glasses of vodka in and this is usually the situation.

At the back of the house, there was a paved patio area that was ideal for this scenario. A few of us sat in a sort of half-circle. I was seated at the farthest extremity, a position where, coincidentally, I could see everyone, and eavesdrop on almost every conversation. There was a table to my right, with a few bottles of vodka and a dozen or so cans, and there were two crates of beer on the ground beside it. Across the patio, near the back door of the house, there was a smaller table where cigarettes were being rolled.

Despite the warm, and welcoming atmosphere, I could find myself starting to venture into my own head. This was always a dangerous point in the evening for me. I would start to disconnect from the crowd as such; there in body but not in spirit.

This wouldn't always be the case. If it were, then I could never enjoy a drink like I do. But one in every few nights, I would have an evening like this where I would overthink and over-analyse a lot of things, past and present. I've seen it happen to others too; 'the drink' can do funny things to us.

It was something I couldn't help. Supposedly, alcohol slows down the nerve cells in our brains; that's why we stagger and slur our words. But I noticed through my own practical trials that my thoughts would often speed up and become more prominent when I was in this state. Given an evening like this, I would usually wake up the following morning, hungover as ever, with a declaration that I would never drink again.

My friends never took these Conor Nolan Public Service Announcements seriously and would wager that it would take a maximum of maybe ten days for me to get the flavour again.

However, this night was the setting of one of my more memorable lows. It could have been tiredness or stress;

I'll never know. But I found myself with a half-empty glass, staring at the ground, completely oblivious to the crowd around me. My mind was racing and bubbling with unexpected thoughts.

I eventually snapped out of my daze for a moment. As I raised my glass to take a drink, I saw that a new addition had arrived. He must have been a friend of Luke's, given that he seemed to know everyone else that was present. As the greetings and small talk subsided, he took a seat and began conversing with a few girls to my left. I paid no real heed, and turned my attention back to my emptying glass, before making the short trip to the table for a refill.

I joined my friend, Ciaran, as he opened another bottle. He wasted no time, as he couldn't take his attention away from the Spotify shuffle; the man always prided himself as the DJ of the evening and would hate to see anyone dissatisfied with the musical ambience. He had playlists for every atmosphere, it seemed.

As I sat back down, the girls to my left had ventured elsewhere. Through the obscured glass in the bathroom window, I saw a head drop to the height of the cistern, move from right to left, and rise again. I laughed quietly to myself; it was very subtle, the whole operation. I was brought up with an extremely negative outlook on drugs, but it's something that I grew out of.

My attention returned to the ground floor, as Luke's friend moved a few seats over and sat to my left.

"You're Conor?" he asked, with a bubbling enthusiasm, far from the stable platform of sober.

I turned to him, trying to respond with the same energy, albeit exceedingly difficult. "Indeed. You must be

8

one of Luke's friends," I replied, moving my right hand over to shake his.

He told me his own name, but amidst the loud music, the laughing company, and Ciaran arguing with one of the girls that Audis are no longer prestigious due to the fact that, and I quote him directly, "Everyone and their aunt has one", I didn't catch it. I hate asking people to repeat themselves, and I probably would have stuttered or slurred if I tried. So, in an attempt to be polite to the gentleman beside me, I pretended to hear him, nodded, and said no more about the matter. But to make the rest of this encounter sound much more profound and mysterious, I'll call him, 'The Stranger'.

"Luke mentioned you a few times. You're like an ambassador for vodka."   "You get used to it, with this crowd here," I replied, as my eyes panned across the scene in front of me. My work colleagues certainly knew how to enjoy an evening.

"Tell me this," he said. "You're the one that competes in powerlifting, aren't you?"

This was one part of the conversation that I was familiar with. Whenever I met someone new, it was only a matter of time before they looked me up and down and questioned my size.

"Yeah, that's me. Tell me, how do you know Luke?" I asked, attempting to divert the conversation in another direction; I was in no mood to start talking about myself.

"I went to school with him, and we played hurling together. Did you ever play?"

I paused and gathered my thoughts for a second.

"I used to play football, but I was nothing special. Although, I would have given my left arm to be."

That wouldn't really have helped, I suppose. It goes to show that in a desperate attempt to be something, you really can shoot yourself in the foot. Regardless, having two arms never made me any good at catching a high ball anyways.

"Was powerlifting your next option then?" he asked.

I ought to say at this point, credit to him for making conversation with me that night. I didn't appear very welcoming, with my thousand-yard stare.

"Kind of. It started as an attempt to get bigger, but then it took over," I answered, as I rested my glass on the arm of the chair.

He sat forward, placing his arms on his thighs, with his bottle clasped between his two hands.

"I have friends who have competed a few times. They're all really calm. But they become like wild animals in the gym. It's crazy."

I laughed quietly to myself. The Stranger wasn't familiar with the emotional side of the sport.

"People get in the zone," I explained. "And adrenaline is running high. So, it's only natural that people get so hyped up. But at the same time, when it comes to releasing anger, there's no sport that compares to it."

"Do you reckon that it's good for the mind?"

I sighed heavily, as I turned my focus back towards him.

"Words don't do it justice, my friend. It's mad what can go through your head in those moments."

"I can't imagine that they're bright and cheerful thoughts."

As I ventured a bit further into myself, I shook my head, clarifying the Stranger's verdict. He remained silent for a moment and took a deep breath before speaking.

"I don't mean to be forward, or intrusive, but since I arrived, you have hardly moved, or even blinked. Is everything ok?"

"I'm ok. I just tend to go into my own head sometimes. Don't worry about it. This isn't the first time it has happened."

He took a box of cigarettes out of his pocket.

"I'm not going to force you, but just so you know, this is what I always do. If ever anyone is in a bad way, I offer to listen. It's my party-piece. I'm like the apprentice counsellor," he told me, as he reached for a lighter.

A smile managed to form despite my cold stare.

"I'm the exact same; I would listen to anyone's problems, and it's usually in a situation like this, as well. I've noticed that it takes a few drinks to get people talking."

The Stranger set light to cigarette number one of the evening. As he exhaled, a small could of smoke followed his breath.

"If that's the case, then I imagine you've preached the importance of talking about things."

I knew where he was going with this; I was at the mercy of my own tactics. "I have, yeah."

He paused once again.

"Hypocrisy is a terrible thing. So, go ahead, and listen to your own advice."

I sat up straight, slightly blindsided by the fact that I hadn't been on this end of the conversation for quite a while.

"I don't even know where to start," I said, laughing. The Stranger removed the cigarette from his mouth.

"When you're out on that stage, or whatever it's called, and you're about to lift, what do you think about?" he asked, with a strong curiosity that made me feel slightly more comfortable; more at ease talking about the delicate matter that is the somewhat unstoppable, and sometimes frightening, train of our thoughts.

My eyes were focused on the ground in front of me.

"The past… I think about being small, and how horrible it was."

I swallowed hard and turned my focus back to the Stranger. He looked me up and down, briefly removing the ash from his cigarette with a flick of his thumb.

"I'm going to guess that that wasn't yesterday or the day before."

"No," I replied, with a shaking head. "It was years ago. I suffered badly with anorexia."

The cigarette's short journey back to the Stranger's mouth was halted, as an element of shock came out to play.

"Ok… no-one's ever spoken to me about that before. Start there."

And with those delicate instructions, he presented me with his box of cigarettes. Now, to be honest, I've never smoked, and I never will. I've always been surrounded by smokers, yet I've never once felt tempted to try it, but for some bizarre reason, I found a certain comfort in having a cigarette between my fingers. Maybe I had been watching too much *Peaky Blinders*.

"Thank you," I replied, as I took one from the box, and held it unlit in my right hand.

The Stranger offered me his lighter.

"No, it's ok, I don't need that."

I patiently awaited judgement for the fact that I wasn't actually going to use the cigarette for its intended purpose.

"You don't smoke?"

I gazed at the white and orange bullet that I held between my index finger and my thumb.

"No," I answered, as I held the cigarette out in front of me. "I'm going to show you something with this. But it'll take a while. Just bear with me."

The Stranger sighed, as he sat back in his chair.

"Fair enough. Whatever you need to do. So, go on, whenever you're ready."

He ushered me with his hand to continue talking, so I sat forward and prepared myself. He had never heard about anorexia before, so I had to explain it fully. This is where it all started.

2

Subtle but Sinister

I remember this very well; too well you could say.

When I was about ten, football was my obsession. It was the only thing that I really cared about. Like a lot of young lads, I sat watching the Sunday Game thinking, 'That'll be me one day', stepping out in Croke Park. A good point to make here is that aiming low has never been my strong point.

However, team-mates that I played with in school soon showed me that I had neither the talent nor the brain for a football field. I couldn't read the game in the way that those around me could, which was one thing that I always envied, because it was something that you couldn't really learn or teach.

I didn't let this get to me, however; there are ways around everything. An element of my father's wisdom comes into play here. He has a very set outlook on life; one of his main principles is that you are only entitled to the things that you truly earn, and over time, he instilled a strong sense of work ethic in me. So, I took this attitude and applied it to my situation.

There are two elements to football, or at least, that's how I saw it through my young and naive eyes. There's the technical side and the physical side. So, as I took a step back from this metaphorical drawing board, on which I had formed a mosaic of failed passes and badly timed tackles, I decided that improving my physical abilities was the best plan.

I hadn't a clue about nutrition, or recovery, or anything of that nature. At the end of the day, I was ten. So, I just started running. One mile turned into two, then three, and then four; it's a lot on a child's body. I started to look in the mirror a lot more often. I was by no means overweight, but for some obscure reason, I never saw myself as being, as they say, 'in good shape'. Regardless, I didn't really care about my image in that sense. I wanted to be faster, and sharper. This was about efficiency and not appearance.

Over time, I saw improvements, and I began to feel a lot better in myself. I was slimming down, but I was at that age where you start to stretch out anyway, so no-one really noticed. I was trying to keep this whole 'fitness regime' under the radar.

I've often found that inspiration can come out of nowhere.

I didn't know what a press-up was until I watched 'Coach Carter'. Samuel L. Jackson's profound motives and speeches are enough to inspire anyone, but seeing those young basketball players put themselves through physical torture for the good of a future goal stayed with me. If they could do it, why couldn't I?

At some point in... God, it must be about ten years ago now, 2009, I spent every evening running till my lungs shrivelled up. Immediately after that, I would do press-ups and sit-ups until I couldn't move. That, in my head, was my one-way ticket to becoming better at something that I loved.

My perception of body image was limited, to say the least, and I had a very vague idea of this concept of the 'ideal body' that most people longingly think about. But after twelve months or so, I had built it. Standing in the mirror in front of me was a level of muscle definition that young men four or five years older than me would have probably envied. What came parallel to this was finding my feet on the pitch. I was becoming more confident in my abilities, and simply better as a player with every match that came and went.

One of the best books I've ever read is 'The Subtle Art of Not Giving A Fuck', by Mark Manson. He makes a point that the mind, when not faced with reasonable problems, will go out of its way to create its own predicaments. I encountered that problem myself. You see, everyone's childhood is different, and I'm blessed to be able to say that mine was a pleasant one. It was an invaluable head start; something that many people don't have, and something that many others take for granted. Because of this, I had very little to ever worry about. So, the bulk of my happiness was solely influenced by what was happening on the field.

As the calendar turned to 2011, I began to play among the under-fourteens. This was where the differences started to show themselves. You were at puberty's mercy, and you really could end up as a child among men. Despite my progress, by the age of twelve, it became clear

16

that I wasn't growing at the same rate as my team-mates. My hunt for manifesting this vision of becoming a brilliant athlete was hindered by one problem.

An unwanted visitor had shown up; a Monkey that had burrowed his way into my head. He travelled light. The only tools he needed in order to do his freelance work, were two gold cymbals.

Through my 'fitness regime', I had sort of stumbled across a diet plan that wasn't on paper, and that wasn't recommended by anyone. I had worked out a daily intake of food; a set number of meals, with a concrete number of bits and pieces in between, that allowed me to 'perform optimally', or so I thought. Fruit and bread were staples, and 'junk food' was nowhere to be seen on this plan. I had gotten used to counting calories and had set myself a daily limit.

The Monkey had convinced me that if I exceeded this daily limit, even by a small number, then I would gain fat as a result. I couldn't have that, since I thought that gaining fat would slow me down and negatively impact my performance. This delicate hypothesis was far from biologically correct, of course, and it was all taking place in my head. But your own head can be the world's most dangerous arena.

As my appetite naturally increased, my daily limit didn't change, and I would often go hungry to stick by the Monkey's rules. It's a chilling thought to look back at lunchtimes in school, feeling hungry even before the bell rang to return to class.

Leaving primary school, I looked frail. I wasn't just as wide and sturdy as my male comrades. My face was narrow, and my neck was slim.

My parents became worried, and my father rightfully voiced his concern. He would logically insist that I eat more, but the Monkey would just clap the cymbals a bit louder during those moments to drown him out. Little did he know, there were some awfully sinister thoughts brewing in my head. I was going through very subtle changes that even I wasn't fully aware of.

The Stranger exhaled heavily as I paused to gather my words.

I took a drink, in synchronisation with two gentlemen who had sat down to the Stranger's left, in the middle of my recollection. They were blissfully unaware of the deep-sea mental diving that I was in the middle of. Lifting the cigarette to his mouth, the Stranger gathered his thoughts.

"You were obsessed beyond belief," he said, evidently shaken by, I suppose I could say, memory number one.

I nodded quietly, as my vision briefly moved towards my own cigarette that I rolled through my fingers.

"It started as an obsession; a positive one in my eyes. But the route to my goal took a sinister turn. I didn't know how to react. I didn't even know what was happening. I just blindly followed the Monkey's orders."

The Stranger nodded, before taking a drink.

"It happened so quickly as well. It just seems as if it started from nowhere." He was right.

It <u>can</u> come out of nowhere.

18

As I lifted my glass, I delved back into my thoughts for a second or two, stirring the over-boiling pot of the past.

"You know this whole idea that whatever doesn't kill us makes us stronger?" The Stranger nodded and allowed me to continue.

"Well, as generic and overused as the idea may be, it's true. It can't be explained any better than that. That is the summary of our lives. A calm sea never made a skilled sailor."

"In other words, blessings described as hardships," he replied, before returning the cigarette to his mouth.

I nodded in agreement.

The Stranger had put me at ease in a noticeably short time frame. He showed a certain open-mindedness, and I felt like I could say what I wanted to, or perhaps, in this case, needed to. As a people, we often feel that we haven't got the right to speak out and express ourselves.

Sometimes, all it takes is for one person to listen.

He sat back once more, allowing me some breathing space to continue my recollection.

"Go on then," he said, smiling. "You have the floor again."

I snapped out of my momentary daze. Now, where was I?

3

Possessed

In the summer of 2011, things only went downhill.

I had become obsessed with my appearance, and the mirror became an enemy. I was obsessed with muscularity, and the grand aim was to decrease my body fat as much as possible. It was becoming wildly unhealthy. Obsession is not always a bad thing, but in this sinister scenario, it was treacherous.

Every day I would exercise for hours. In the morning I would do push-ups and sit-ups, in the afternoon I would run, and then, in the evening, I'd either have team training, or I would meet friends for a kick-about. I would do anything to avoid sitting down.

It became like a job; almost like clocking up hours in the workplace, with the Monkey as my manager. The Monkey had convinced me that this regime was a daily requirement, so if by some divine reason I would miss out on a "day's work" worth of exercise, I would find myself crippled by my thoughts. I would overthink and over analyse. Would I gain fat if I slowed down? Would I lose pace, or underperform? The Monkey was preying on my athletic goals to make me follow his rules.

I had a mission statement somewhere in my mind. The goal was to, every week, exercise more and consume less. It was a sick mindset that I was in, and an obscene life that I was living.

I've made sense of it all in the years since. You see, anorexia is a way of finding control. If you can't find control in your life in general, you may turn to finding it within your own circle, for instance, with your image and weight. I don't know what it was that made me feel like I didn't have enough control already; if I knew, it would have made life much simpler. Perhaps it was the fear of starting secondary school and entering an unfamiliar environment. I'll never know. But I do remember the powerful feeling of being in command and being in charge of one's own life.

It's ironic in so many ways. In a sense, you're fully in control, because you are doing this to your own body. But it's not you. You're possessed; a helpless puppet on the Monkey's string. But you can't see that. He distracts you from his sinister plan by gifting you with a growing addiction; an addiction to the feeling of control. The hardest part of all was not eating when I felt hungry. That was the Monkey's toughest rule. But when I followed it, it gave me the most satisfaction. Why? Because willpower is our most basic form of control.

Food became my worst enemy. Because of the set number of daily calories that I would allow myself, I had to plan where the next meal would come from at all times. I had a rough approximation in my head of the calorie content of most everyday foods, but I would always round up just to be safe. I had this horrible fear of excess food being put in front of me, so, in the case of a bigger serving, I just wouldn't clear the plate. Every time, I would leave slightly more behind; the Monkey was extremely intelligent and would come up with ingenious ways for me to eat less without raising suspicion.

My parents became terribly concerned and called me out on my appearance time and time again. I looked tired constantly, with large bags under my eyes, and my clothes were slowly starting to hang off me. My father used to say that I looked like an abused labourer; someone being run into the ground on a building site, on the end of a shovel, or a wheelbarrow. I suppose, in a way, he was right. Except for the fact that my foreman lived in my head... and worked for free.

I remember my grand-parents being present one day during one of these often-had conversations. They were worried also. I panicked at the thought of them stepping in and giving their opinion because, if they did, they could spark several changes. Change would mean that I would lose all control. And that was the underlying fear. So, when they spoke to me about the matter, the Monkey clapped louder. And when they spoke to my parents, I broke into a cold sweat. It's a twisted fantasy. You end up living in a home-made horror film.

As the summer progressed, my mother became sick with worry. Through tears, she questioned me. Realistically, I wanted to break down and tell her everything; that I was starving myself, that I was running myself into the ground, and that I was beginning to hate my existence. But those words couldn't form themselves, and in the echoes of the Monkey's clapping, I found a template speech stating that everything was ok and that I felt great. In simple terms, the Monkey was a spontaneous, silver-tongued, and stubborn individual.

Coming into the autumn of 2011, my bodyweight fell dramatically. On the football field, I felt weak; my pace was starting to disappear, and I couldn't run against the wind. If I ran any more than twenty yards before attempting to pass or shoot, I wouldn't be able to lift my legs to do so. I could barely raise my arms to catch the ball over my head. This was a serious problem because I was now going backwards on the goal that I had originally set out to achieve.

My off-field progress was spot on, however. I was losing weight by the day. This was becoming far more important; the real priorities had truly fallen. Only a mental illness could take my eye off something that meant so much to me.

All I wanted to see in the mirror was bone. It sends a shiver through me to think back; lifting my arms to count my ribs and placing my hands on my face to feel a jawbone that was coming out through my skin. I remember looking at the movement of the bones in my hands as I opened and closed my fist, proud of what I was achieving. I was sick, and mentally broken. My neurological 'check engine' light was burning brightly.

You see, when you're underweight, some gruesome stuff happens. Your organs can't properly function. Your lungs don't work fast enough, so breathing becomes a problem. Your heart physically can't beat fast enough for strenuous activity. Your body can't efficiently convert food to energy, so you don't heat up. That was the one thing that got to me; running for sixty minutes in a game, and not breaking a bead of sweat. You constantly feel cold; the slightest breeze leaves you frozen. You truly are weak, vulnerable, and to be honest, scared. You're aware that your body is going into shutdown, but the Monkey stops you from saving your own life; the cymbals just get louder.

In August 2011, I played my last football game before getting help. By this point, I was down to about thirty-five kilos, which for a five-foot-three male, is the equivalent of a walking skeleton. In a year, I had gone from being physically fit and healthy, to a frail, fragile mess. Playing that last game, I was useless; officially redundant at the one thing that I loved.

That match was the turning point; a sign from life that I needed help. To this day I have never forgotten that feeling of absolute weakness. I had hit rock bottom. If I lost any more weight, I was probably going to die. After a hastily organised visit to the doctor, I was referred to a counsellor.

Till the day I die, I will never forget that first session. As I sat down, with my parents by my side, I just remember thinking to myself, 'Here you are now. This is how much weight you've lost. This is rock bottom.' And the most horrible fact of all is that I was proud of myself.

The Stranger sat with a calm focus as I recalled my broken mind.

"It's one of those things that you hear about," he said, as he unzipped his jacket. "But being honest, I never gave it any thought before. I understand the severity of it all, but looking in on it from the outside, it's hard to grasp. In the sense that... you really wonder why someone would starve themselves. But hearing it straight from you, a victim, puts it into perspective."

He was right.

It's the kind of thing that you need to hear straight from the horse's mouth to truly understand.

"Looking back, I still don't even understand it myself," I replied. "It just takes over. But one thing is for sure; it's amazing what counselling can do."

The Stranger removed the ash from his cigarette.

"I know a few people who swear by it. They reckon that telling everything to a complete stranger is far easier. There's no judgement, and there's more anonymity to it."

As he returned the cigarette to his mouth, I wondered if he knew at that moment that he was doing a good job himself. I felt that I could safely speak in his presence. Like he said, there was a sense of anonymity. He was the momentary embodiment of the perfect stranger.

"At first it was an absolute disaster," I explained. "I sat opposite the counsellor and a paediatrician. I knew that they all meant well, but it was intimidating. It felt as if everyone was analysing my response, hanging on my every word."

"I imagine it took time to adjust, and to get your thoughts out."

My eyes met the ground again.

"Indeed, it did. After leaving the first session, my father honestly couldn't understand what had just happened. He was worried for me but angered by the situation. He asked repeatedly why I had done such a thing; why had I put myself in this situation? Replying in tears, all I could say was that I didn't know. That was all I could say. That's what makes anorexia so detrimental. How do you fix a sinking ship when there's no sign of water coming in?"

I turned my attention back towards the Stranger, who was becoming a bit more emotionally attached to my story.

"This really stood between you and your father."

"It did... It tore things apart. But his reaction was to be expected. This was something that he, and most of his generation, had never encountered before."

"What about your mother?"

"My mother was my rock through the whole ordeal," I replied, smiling. "She was literally the glue that held everything together. No amount of money could ever adequately repay her for everything that she has done. It's the same in many families, I've realised. Not all, but many. A mother's work never ends and is rarely fully appreciated."

My eyes wandered throughout the garden for a few seconds. As I left my thoughts and returned to the present, the music became louder in my ears. Everyone else's conversations slowly trickled into one collective glass of indistinct chit-chat. Laughter seemed to fill the air, and everyone seemed to be in good spirits. A few people went back and forth past the Stranger and I, heading for the 'booze table', yet no-one interrupted us.

It was as if we weren't there.

As I finished my detour, I turned back to the conversation. "Do you know that phrase, 'having a screw loose'?" I asked. "Do you feel like it was applicable?"

"I remember saying to my mother, not that long ago, that I truly believe, in all honesty, that we all have a screw loose. Nobody's perfectly mentally stable. It's not possible. But some of us are just in a better place than others. Sometimes, like an engine, a fan-belt wears thin. A head gasket builds up pressure over time. A gearbox gets worn down. An engine needs care and consideration, and when it's not looked after, a professional must intervene. The mind is the same. Sometimes, in our lifetime, we may need a qualified mechanic to step in and fix this complex combustion chamber that they call the brain. It's amazing how the right help can change everything."

I paused to take a drink and try to find my words.

"I was in very good hands in counselling; I had all the help I needed. But whether or not I was going to accept the help that was being presented to me, was another question."

4

Rewiring

In counselling, we delved deep into my thoughts, and my relationship with food was analysed.

Even with expert help, I made no progress in the first month. I couldn't break out of my crooked way of thinking. It was as if I was afraid of losing what I'd 'earned'. The Monkey had invested a lot of effort in me, moulding me as its puppet, so it wouldn't let me turn my life around without a fight. All exercise had been banned, so my endorphin rush had been put on hold. I fell into a deep depression, and this shone through quite quickly in counselling. I hit my lowest point one night in October 2011. For the one and only time in my life, I verbally said the words, "I see no point in being alive anymore". Needless to say, I was put on a regular dosage of an antidepressant called 'Prozac' fairly soon after. It's like serotonin on a spoon. A liquid to keep my thoughts out of the suicidal realm.

Things were falling apart, living in my self-made prison. Every passing day started to feel longer. The Monkey's clapping kept ringing in my ears, till eventually, I cracked. I had to change, and simply accept all the help I was being given. So, after six weeks of no weight gain, I began to talk more openly in counselling. I slowly began to explain my thought process, and how I felt about food and my appearance.

In an attempt to gain weight, I started taking supplement drinks, and I slowly became open to the idea of eating more. By Christmas, roughly eight weeks later, I was approaching something resembling a healthy appearance. I had more energy, a more positive outlook on life, and a renewed spring in my step. I could now see the end of the tunnel. I could see myself back on a football field, happy again.

During this time, my family was supportive beyond belief. However, my relationship with my father began to feel the pressure. You see, the problem with anorexia is in the healing process. It's not a case of just feeding the victim, like people think, but rather, a priority to allow the mind in question time to adjust to the new eating patterns that it's being introduced to. The mind is so corrupted into a set way of thinking that it needs time to evolve to a healthier state. In other words, the Monkey doesn't die straight away, you just break his cymbals. My father didn't really see this. He would insist that I force-feed myself to get me out of this predicament ASAP. I understand now completely when I look back.

He didn't want me to remain in poor health any longer, and on top of that, he didn't want 'the parish' to see me in poor health. That was another problem. He didn't really understand that the physical state I was in was a manifestation of a mental disorder. Do I blame him for his lack of understanding? Of course not. Mental illness is not a popular topic of discussion in this country, so there was no way that any of us could properly perceive the situation.

Moving into the latter part of my first year of secondary school, counselling continued. Now that I was at a healthier weight, priority shifted towards maintaining this newfound healthy mindset towards food. We did a lot of work on body image and being comfortable with one's own physical appearance. The way my counsellor did it was by placing me in front of a mirror. She would then trace out, on the mirror, the image that I could see, by my visual guidance.

The principle is, if you have body dysmorphia of any kind, whilst in that mind-frame, the mirror can play tricks on you. It can tease you into believing that you don't look as big, or small, as you actually are, depending on which end of the dysmorphia 'spectrum' you find yourself. I was thirteen, coming into a vain and self-obsessed age group where the mirror inevitably ends up becoming a life coach for a lot of young people.

There was a worry that through the self-analysis that comes with puberty, I would slip back into my old ways. But they needn't have worried. By this time, now the summer of 2012, my mindset had resumed a healthier state. I had re-found my previous motives.

Re-emerging back onto the pitch after so many months away was life-changing. I never wanted to end up back in a self-made cage. I made a vital promise to myself, at thirteen, to never be weak again. I had tasted the sour flavour of physical incapability, and I swore blind to never return.

The Stranger smiled, as my bitter memories began to show a slight hint of hope.

"So, you were in the clear," he said, as he sat forward slightly. I hesitated for a second with my eyes focused on my glass.

"I suppose. In a sense, I was living as a child again for the first time in years. I was no longer thinking about weighing scales, or a mirror. I was free for once, in some sense. And for the first time in a long time, I was genuinely relaxed."

As I lifted my eyes towards the Stranger, he displayed a look of confusion.

"I honestly thought it'd last a bit longer. I was led to believe that anorexia lasts for a few years normally."

I rolled the cigarette between my fingers, with a cautious grip, so as not to tear the delicate white coating.

"In hindsight, yes. It did only last twelve months. That was how long I stayed in counselling before being discharged. It does stay with people a lot longer than that. In girls, it can be deadly; I've heard of cases lasting up to five years."

I paused, shivering at the thought of being at the Monkey's mercy for that long.

"You're right though, in a sense," I continued. "I wasn't fully free. I still kept a mental recall of my daily food intake, and I would still get slightly anxious if I didn't exercise for a couple of days. But I was comfortable with where I was; grateful to be in a healthier frame of mind."

The Stranger thought for a second. Looking around at a scene that wasn't showing any signs of changing, he took in everything that I had said.

"Were you afraid that you were never going to fully recover? That this mindset would never fully leave?"

I stopped breathing for a split second.

My mind flashed back to my reflection all those years ago; my face so thin that my teeth were coming out through the skin above my upper lip.

"The Monkey's cymbals were broken. But with the... the metal shards of my past he could still form a quiet tune... a tune that would stay there. And at the time, I will admit, I was afraid that I would never fully be free."

The Stranger placed his left elbow on the arm of the chair and supported his head in his hand.

"What about life outside your own head?" he asked.

"I got picked on a lot for being small. I could never use the word 'bullied'... at the time... because the abuse would often come from those who disguised themselves as my friends. You can't really label someone as a bully in your own mind when, some of the time, they are being pleasant. It's hard to stand up to enemies, but even harder to stand up to friends."

I could feel the blood rushing through my head as my breathing became slower.

I had forgotten what it felt like to be disrespected. An echo of laughter tunnelled through my mind. It had been so long, but I could still hear them.

Reaching for his bottle, the Stranger remained silent for a few seconds. I think he knew that he had hit a nerve. My thoughts swallowed me for a moment or two. As I returned to the present, the static of my memories was replaced by the HD volume of my good friends. I was channel-hopping between the horror film in my head and the comedy around me.

"When you think of laughter, what comes to mind?" I asked. He lowered his cigarette, slightly baffled by the question.

"Good times. Being around people you care about... and having a few drinks. That's what laughter reminds me of."

I nodded, in understanding rather than agreement.

"Laughter is a universal language. Mr Bean made the world laugh without saying a word. Laughter can be a form of appreciation. Laughter can represent companionship and comradery, care and closeness. Laughter can bring complete strangers together... Listen; listen to the conversations around you right now. These are the good times that you described."

I paused, looking across the patio, over the Stranger's shoulder.

"But laughter has a sinister side. Laughter can be an expression of disregard, disrespect, and condescension. Laughter can play with your mind. Laughter can stay with you."

As the horror film in my head briefly came to life, I could see over the Stranger's shoulder, lined up against the garden wall, those who took comedic advantage of 'small Conor'. As the insensitivity of many people   walked itself collectively to the podium of my verbal expression, I somehow found a way to put the pain into words.

"When I was in counselling, I was so heavily influenced by the help that I got, that it almost felt as if my brain had been rewired. It's amazing what the right help can do… But there are people I've come across who have also tried to rewire me; to make me think differently. You see, not everyone that tries to change you, or mould you, has your best interests at heart… Remember that… Some of them want to prove a point; to have control and to convince you that you are below them, at the bottom of a meaningless social pyramid. They want to crush your self-esteem… and self-belief, to belittle the chances of you rising up, and being 'better than them', or climbing higher than them in this bullshit stratification system; a system held in high regard by…by shallow… self-obsessed people."

The Stranger allowed a second or two of leeway for me to compose myself, and perhaps, for his own aural digestion.

"How… and why… did you think of this?"

He could comprehend that my mind was working overtime. I finished my drink, before looking into my empty glass.

"I gave this a lot of thought. Giving a lot of thought requires a lot of time. But I have had all the time I need to think about these things. Because there are some things in life that will truly… truly never leave."

After a brief silence, he got up and headed for the table. He opened a bottle for himself, refilled my glass also, and returned. As I rested my fresh glass on the arm of the chair, I took a moment to think.

Maybe those poltergeists of the past envied me now; perhaps for the great people that I had around me. One thing was for certain though.

They would never envy the mental burdens that I had carried on their behalf.

5

The Monkey's Funeral

As the Stranger and I shared a drink in unison, he slowly analysed the anecdotes that I had presented to him, his eyes scanning the garden as he thought. Removing the cigarette from his mouth, he turned his attention back to me.

"You mentioned that your father was worried that 'the parish' would see you in poor health. Would people not understand? I mean, fair enough, the older generation aren't very clued into the world of mental health, but surely people would understand in general. As you said, it's no-one's fault. It's the Monkey."

I laughed quietly. The Stranger was clearly a native of the big city, unfamiliar with the complex mechanics of a small town.

"My father knew something that I would learn over time. He was familiar with the merciless reality where people talk and stir the pot. It wouldn't matter if I walked around with a nametag saying, 'I am anorexic'. Somewhere along the line, the story would get twisted, and somebody would start a rumour that I wasn't being fed. Because you see, news in a small village is like a game of Chinese Whispers played by a thousand people, and you can be sure that the thousandth person is going to hear something that doesn't even partially resemble the truth. It's the main reason that I hate where I come from. I love my family, but I hate the small-town mindset."

The Stranger was taken aback by my response "People are hardly that crooked, are they?"

"You don't know the half of it," I replied, shaking my head and trying to calm my frustration. "There are some countryside people who would make great journalists, capable of spinning a story out of thin air, my friend."

"Fair enough. But more importantly, how were things with your father when you got back to good health?"

"Better. He's a builder by trade, but he's more than that. He's a genius, in fairness to him. He could take the lid off one of those bottles with the bucket of a digger. Because of all that, our house is his castle. Around it, there are hand-built stone walls that took a couple of years to finish. So, lending a hand with all this was a way of winning back his respect, as such."

"So, you had made peace with him." I looked at my cigarette as I sighed heavily.

"Not fully, I'm afraid. He was still convinced that I had 'gone against the grain', as he says. But I was happy enough to have the chance to rebuild things with him, pardon the pun. There was learning in all of this. He always instilled in me that you must earn what you get and that you have to fight for what you want. So, as I happily spent most weekends on the end of a shovel, I could appreciate his lessons. It was much more satisfying to look out your kitchen window at a scene that you yourself had created."

The Stranger took a drag on his cigarette as he listened.

"Anyway," I said, "I had other problems that were starting to show their true colours. History was repeating itself."

As a young man, I suppose fourteen is when puberty really can play games with you. When you look around, your male peers are either six feet tall with a beard, or they still look twelve; there isn't really any middle ground.

I hadn't really grown since getting back to full health, and my weight was showing no signs of increasing. I was still keeping a mental record of my food intake; still holding myself back slightly. The Monkey was still making quiet silhouettes in the back of my mind. I remained fragile, and the development gap between me and my teammates was becoming more noticeable, for the second time in two years.

As my comrades grew tall and strong, I remained the runt of the litter. In 2013, we formed an amalgamation with two other football clubs. Going to the first few team meetings, and training sessions, I became anxious. I didn't cope well around my own age group, often feeling judged, and condescended. I could deal with adults, largely due to the fact that I respected my elders and would see myself as the automatic inferior in every conversation.

On the other hand, with my peers, I had to talk to them as equals, which was something I couldn't do. I didn't have the confidence to stand up tall and demand respect. It was always lurking in the back of my mind that so many people didn't take me seriously, and I felt it only plausible for these new comrades of mine to jump on that bandwagon.

Up until this point, I had never been left out of the starting eleven, thirteen, or fifteen of a team for very long. With this new amalgamated squad, I had to squeeze into the top fifteen, out of twenty-five candidates. It became clear that I hadn't a hope; a player who was just too small. I don't hold grudges over decisions, and I wasn't angry about being left as a substitute; I was angry because of the disrespect. Other teammates of mine were called by name, appreciated and praised. I felt that I wasn't even given feedback, despite working as hard as they did. It felt like I was unnoticed, and left to one side. Sport can be ruthless like that, and when you're simply not good enough, then you're forgotten about. Life is tough, and I accepted that.

But what I couldn't accept was that I was starting to notice a bit of a life pattern. I was the backup, it seemed. Someone people talked to when everyone else had left the room. Someone who made the starting fifteen when everyone else broke their legs. I was a second choice.

Why couldn't I just be as good as everyone else? Why had anorexia set me back?

Why couldn't I just be normal?

I was young, upset, and confused.

Sport is regarded as one of the biggest factors in the mental health of young people, supposedly as a form of exercise, a boost for self-confidence, and a social icebreaker. Team sports are glorified as CV gold, showing your abilities to work with others, and communicate well. And I absolutely agree.

What isn't talked about, however, in schools or in dressing rooms, is the detrimental impact it has on a young individual to be left to one side and forgotten about.

Sport is an escape for so many people. It's impossible to know what a young teenager is getting away from when they step onto a pitch. Maybe they don't excel in school, and the football field is the one place where they feel successful. Maybe it's an escape from a broken family or even a broken mind. The adolescent faces plenty of challenges on an everyday basis. The last thing they need is to have their safe place contaminated by inconsiderate management, egotistical teammates, and insensitive spectators.

But we'll say no more about that. That's bad marketing, I suppose.

This very honest recollection left me feeling slightly numb in the moment. My grip tightened on my glass as I took a drink, before my eyes returned themselves to the ground. As I lowered my glass, the coldness of the concrete's surface was a subtle and sinister reminder of the substitute's dug-out, a place where the aspirations of many could slowly fade into a chilling memory.

"I hadn't started drinking... I had no interest in smoking... Drugs were an urban legend, whose existence I could barely fathom... I was following all the rules. All I knew was hard work. All I knew were goalposts and a ball.

I had nothing else to live for... Football was everything. The foundation of my happiness was being broken beneath my feet."

For the first time all evening, I lifted my head to look up into the darkening sky.

The Stranger joined me in my spaced-out stare.

"They say that everything happens for a reason. Given the gift of hindsight, was that the case?"

I moved my eyes back to my glass as I rotated it on the arm of the chair. "I suppose... like every situation, life has its reasoning. I hadn't a clue what that reasoning was at the time, but life was teaching me lessons about rejection, and coping with failure. Not being good enough is a hard pill to swallow."

"You talk in a very, I suppose, spiritual way. Are you religious, by any chance?"

"My father's side of the family is particularly insistent on religion," I replied. "I only go to mass when I have to, to keep the peace, as such; but I noticed a few things over the years. I was seeing a lot of corrupt people portraying themselves as saints. Don't get me wrong, I don't disagree with religion itself. We all need to have faith in something, and what you have faith in is up to you. And if that's God, then, by all means, keep going."

I paused for a second, as I thought back to staged conversations with a handful of hypocrites.

"But it seemed to me that some people used this invisibility cloak of being religious to cover up who they really are. For some people, it was just a front; it was all image. From my own experience, I can safely say that I have met some of the most heart-warming and genuine

41

people in my life around tables covered in cocaine and ketamine. But at the same time, I have shaken hands with some awfully despicable people on a Sunday morning. It's amazing what a small parish can keep secret. It would seem that Chinese Whispers can work in some people's favour."

The Stranger laughed quietly.

"A simple 'no' would have done. But anyway, go on."

I moved away from religion, and back to the dilemma of life's lessons and reasoning.

"It became clear to me that if I didn't get bigger, then I could forget any aspirations that I had regarding a football field, and any other desires that I had of being taken seriously, or at least respected. Anorexia, and being the runt of the litter, had taken enough from me. So, in the summer of 2013, just over two years after the Monkey had first burrowed into my head, I put a bullet between his two eyes."

"You were finally free from it," he replied, smiling.

"Finally," I whispered. "I had had enough of being possessed."

The Stranger returned the cigarette to his mouth, as his own eyes now focused themselves on the ground also. His smile faded. As he turned his focus back to me, he paused for a second, and for the first time that evening, there was a moment of silent eye contact. I felt as if he was becoming more like a friend, than just a stranger at a session.

"Looking back now, would you change anything? Do you wish that it had just never happened?"

I went quiet for a few seconds, as I felt my shoulders drop and my chest loosen. The end of this recollection has always been a bittersweet moment.

"I wouldn't change a thing," I answered. "Everything happens for a reason."

6

The 'Should' Concept

The Stranger and I were quiet for a few moments. I went into deep thought about what was said a few moments before; 'everything happens for a reason'. I couldn't help but smile as another one of life's lessons crept into my head. As I sat up straight, the Stranger came back to reality and we returned to our chat.

"There was something I read once," I explained. "I can't remember where, but it stayed with me. It said that there's a reason that we never find God when times get tough. Why? Because a teacher is always quiet during a test. So, every hardship we go through is a challenge given to us to teach us an overall lesson."

"I agree," he replied, once again cementing the boundless nature of his open-mindedness. He removed the ash from his cigarette, and swiftly resumed his undivided attention.

"What lesson did life have for you this time?"

"Life had a lesson for me about gratitude, I suppose, and about the way we think. Basically, when I was fourteen, I was nearly killed."

The Stranger's exhaled smoke crossed my line of vision. In the brief silence, he lit another cigarette, sparking a curiosity within me as to how he could afford <u>actual</u> ones. The student smokers that I knew engaged in the poor man's struggle of rolling tobacco; a process that seemed to take forever. I've often tried to roll one for a laugh, but I've always failed miserably.

"Go on then," he said, returning the lighter to his pocket, and ushering me to continue.

I sat back and shuffled the deck of my memories.

It was July 9th, 2013; there are some dates we'll never forget. At home, there is a maze of narrow, winding roads; a very typical rural setting. My grandmother's house is not a stone's throw from our own, up on a hill, with a short laneway. The 'main' road itself is just about wide enough for two cars. I used to cycle there, and I had noticed over time that if I descended this lane fast enough, I could reach home in seconds.

Jesus, that sounds childish in hindsight, but anyway.

The problem, though, was that at this speed, I couldn't keep to my own side. I would end up at the bottom of the lane, right in the crosshairs of oncoming traffic, if there was any. Most days the roads were empty, and this stunt of mine would be safe.

But on this fateful day, it was a different case. I wish that it had been caught on camera, given that it was timed to perfection. I reached the road and crashed head-on into a neighbour of mine. He was a family friend and a real gentleman. In the moment, when I saw him there not ten yards away from me, I tried to turn to my right in an attempt to cross the hedge on the other side of the road. This meant that

I was hit from the side and thrown onto his windscreen. Bouncing off, I was left covered in blood and sprawled out on the tarmac.

According to family, the neighbour in question ran up to my grandmother's house and came in with the profound announcement that I may have been killed, however, I certainly can't blame his poor phrasing, given the severity of the situation.

I regained consciousness, maybe a minute or so later, with my uncle standing over me in a cold sweat. It was like being awakened in the middle of the night; it takes you a few seconds to gather your thoughts and suss out where you are and what year it is.

I'll never forget looking down at what had been a white t-shirt, now destroyed with blood, and seeing my bicycle demolished. It had made it to the far side of the road, ironically. An ambulance had been called, and I had been instructed not to move, for fear of doing further damage.

As the road filled with neighbours and family, I began to go into my own head, asking myself all the wrong questions.

What if my legs were broken? What if I was disabled?

Was this how it ended?

Was I never to step on a football field again, because of one mistake?

I was in bits and couldn't think straight. The ambulance arrived and I was rushed to hospital, tied to a huge wooden board that left me unable to move. I still couldn't feel any pain, which I didn't know whether to view as a relief or a disaster.

As I was x-rayed, there was a feeling of loneliness. You start to realise that you're on your own and that it's all out of your hands. A tear or two left my eye.

The x-ray lasted less than two minutes, but it felt like days.

As the doors re-opened, a sense of relief washed over me, and I was taken into one of the wards. There was a three-hour wait before I got the results. My mother was there with me, in a far worse state than I was. To be honest, I wasn't even thinking, just trying to somehow comprehend what had happened.

A nurse arrived back with the news and, according to her, I was fine. No broken bones and no permanent damage, just severe bruising, and a few 'lacerations' that needed stitching. Supposedly, they are deep tears in the flesh, I later found out with a bit of googling.

After she had left, a doctor appeared. Unbeknownst to myself, I was slowly bleeding out of the back of my head while this man was standing there. He looked me up and down, with a clipboard in his hand, and came to a vital diagnosis.

"You should have worn a helmet," he informed me, and left.

From that moment on, I fully believed the claim that behind every glorified doctor, there's a nurse doing most of the work. But anyway.

The wounds on my head and leg were stitched up, and I was kept in overnight for observation. The following morning, I walked out, granted, in a lot of pain, but I wasn't in a wheelchair. I was on my own two feet. I had never been more grateful for the ability to stand up in all my days. I had never been more grateful to simply be alive.

I snapped out of my consuming recollection and saw that the Stranger was a bit shaken, to say the least. This was the reaction I had been hoping for. There was a certain pride that I took in shocking people; entertaining those around us is one thing but leaving them speechless is another ball game.

"You're lucky to be alive. You should have been killed, or at least disabled," he stammered.

I shuffled in my chair a bit before posing my argument.

"I never liked the word 'should'. We beat ourselves up over it. It creates an unwanted obligation, pressuring us to feel a certain way or to act in a certain manner. It's like a subconscious burden, in a sense. We often think that we should be qualified by 22, married by 30, and have a mortgage by 35. Life can tamper with us, giving us false indicators to base our actions and thoughts on, preying on those of us, who hold the mythical 'should' close to heart."

I paused to take a drink and to let my rant sink in.

"Fair enough; in the given scenario, the likelihood does point to me ending up with a broken spine and a cracked skull. But we imagine that likelihood based on common knowledge of what the human body can handle, and other factors like physics and statistics perhaps. And those are all credible arguments. However, my friend, everything happens for a reason. We're all here for a reason. And as far-fetched as this may sound, I believe that reason will keep us alive. That reason is far more powerful than the things that we all think, 'should' happen."

I gave the Stranger a second or two to let all that sink in. Countless times, I had recalled that anecdote, and I had always gotten the same reaction. So, over time, I crafted a counterargument; a bona fide ace to pull out of the deck in the case of a closed mind.

"What makes you believe that a reason kept you alive? Perhaps it was just pure luck."

I sat forward to play my hand.

"Because I thought about it. In two years, I had escaped anorexia, reached a point where my organs should have shut down, taken medicine to stop myself from feeling suicidal, battled depression on a daily basis, and now, to top everything off, I had nearly given a neighbour a heart attack by smashing his windscreen, writing off his van, and almost killing myself in the process. You don't escape anorexia that quickly, like you said yourself. You don't walk away from accidents like that. Life had given me the 'get out of jail' card. Twice. In very quick succession. Perhaps I was here for a reason then. Perhaps we all are. Life couldn't let me die, because I had things to do. I had some reason to be here that I had not yet found."

The Stranger was still slightly perplexed, to say the least.

"Do you really believe that? That we're all here for a reason?"

"It seems very far-fetched when you're twenty years of age, but I fully believe it. Everything happens for a reason. You're here for a reason. And the greatest honour in this life is to find out what that reason is."

He took a drag on his cigarette, before silently gathering his thoughts. His open-mindedness was receiving its most stern test of the evening so far.

"That's the kind of thing you hear motivational speakers talking about; how they found meaning in life, and all that sort of stuff. It's the kind of thing people don't really talk about until they're fifty."

"Believe me," I replied, as I sat back in my chair. "You never know when your purpose is going to show itself; it can fall out of thin air."

I took a drink and got back to the heart of the situation.

"After the accident, I was housebound and hardly able to walk for a month. Five minutes on my feet would leave my chest feeling heavy. It was a reminder; a cold, hard throwback to absolute weakness, and a temporary return to the cage. It was what I needed to make sure that the Monkey never came back to life. I couldn't fall back into this trap; I had to get as far away from being weak as I possibly could. So, I renewed my vows in 2013. I would never be weak again."

"I'm going to guess that you stayed faithful to that promise," he replied as he looked me up and down.

"There was more to it now. There was a fear that hadn't been there before. Life taught me to be grateful for my newfound health. A split-second crash, that could have been avoided if I hadn't been so reckless, ended up being one of the best lessons of my young life."

"It's mad. Inspiration can come in all different forms, can't it?" With that statement, a lightbulb went off in my head.

"Speaking of inspiration, there's one man I need to tell you about."

7

Pressure

One of the greatest influences on my thinking and mentality, growing up, was a man by the name of Eric Thomas. He's probably one of the best motivational speakers in the world. To put it simply and to keep the ball rolling here, he gets through to people, and he most certainly got through to me.

Over in the USA, American football is massive, as you would imagine. It's the nation's pride. I'm not a huge fan, but it's common knowledge that college football is one of the greatest opportunities that an athlete can dream of in The States. It's a direct ticket to becoming a professional.

I'm waffling a small bit but bear with me.

In a speech that he gave to a group of players, Eric made the point to the young men in front of him that they had the opportunity of a lifetime in their hands, commenting on the financial prosperity that was within their grasp.

In essence, he told them that the worst thing in the world is not growing up in poverty. The worst thing in the world is, in fact, coming from poverty, gaining the opportunity to get out, and not taking full advantage of it, and then having to go back to having nothing. That's the worst pain you can feel. Being talked about because you had your chance and lost it. That was the message he gave to these young men, to not lose the invaluable chance that they had.

That was what scared me also; the thought of going back to having nothing. Or in my case, going back to being a skeleton; going back to being possessed. So, at fourteen, in an attempt to run away from the cage, I learned something about life. I learned about the pressure we put on ourselves as people.

You see, not to sound arrogant, but I had always performed well in an academic sense. So, when the Junior Cert rolled around, I felt that I had to step up. But at the same time, I had to build my body to somehow escape this feeling of weakness.

There was a beautiful difference between these two plans.

Everyone expected so much of me in school, so it was imagined that I would do well anyway. No-one would be shocked if I were to ace every exam, so the almost inevitable outcome made it necessary for me to focus, and not let anyone down. However, it also made the process quite mundane. There was no excitement, and to be honest, no real incentive. It was a case of avoiding the failure to live up to my potential, rather than chasing a goal. I was already far up the mountain; I just had to avoid falling off, with a lot to lose, and much less to gain.

Plan number two was a different game of cards; I wanted to be strong. I was about forty-five kilos at almost fifteen years of age; still a walking skeleton. No-one had any belief that I could turn things around. This time, if I failed, I would just be starved of pride and opportunity. But if I succeeded, I could feast on the shock of those who gave me no chance. There was much more incentive, and the goal was bigger; I was at the bottom of a mountain, the height of which I was unaware. There were no limits, and I had absolutely nothing to lose.

"You were getting an insight into, I suppose, internal and external expectations."

"I realised the difference over time; when you achieve something that was pressured upon you from outside, it's a relief. But when you achieve something that has been spurred on by a desire from within, that's fulfilment."

I took a moment to allow a few of my ideas to congregate in my head, ideas that I had explained to people whilst sitting in the Stranger's hot seat, playing the role of the listener.

"There are some things that money can't buy," I explained. "They are love, character, and fulfilment. We all know that you can't buy love, that's a more obvious one, and you certainly can't buy fulfilment. Fulfilment is earned… But character cannot be bought either; in fact, character is priceless. It's found in yourself, and in those around you. You will find it in yourself over time, but you will find it around you at the right time, when you need it most."

As I took a drink, the Stranger soaked in my rehearsed wisdom. "So, how do you describe character?"

I rested my glass on the arm of the chair to allow my hands the freedom to assist me, through gesture, to form this delicate mosaic of meaning.

"Character has three pillars," I answered. "Whenever I found one in myself, I would find it in someone around me as well. Character has a magnetic nature to it. The first pillar is determination. I found this at fourteen, when I set about this plan of 'getting big', or strong, or whatever you want to call it. Now, it did take determination to lose weight when I was twelve, but I won't take any credit away from the Monkey; that was his achievement, not mine."

My forearm spasmed slightly, forcing the opening and closing of my fist to release the tension.

"And did you find the first pillar around you as well?"

"Oh, indeed I did," I replied. "Indeed, I did. I'm very proud to say that the most determined man I've ever met is also one of my best friends. Kyle, or as we would later christen him, 'Clive', was one of the first people that I befriended in secondary school. I had a world of respect for him from the first day I met him. We were different, but very similar at the same time. He wasn't academic, but he was smart in ways that I envied; he was quick-witted and could talk for Ireland. You couldn't argue with him, and on top of that, he's probably the best all-round athlete I've seen to this day. He dominated nearly every sport that the school had on offer… but despite being this… humorous nephew of Superman, we had one thing in common."

"And what was that?" he asked, as I stopped in my tracks to once again structure the past in my mind.

"Our greatest... you could say, bonding leverage, was that we both knew the pain of being laughed at... and being brushed aside in conversation."

"It's amazing how our hardships can bring us together as people, isn't it?"

The Stranger's accuracy could not have been placed on a high enough pedestal with a statement like that.

"His family are in the forestry business," I continued. "He got involved in this quite young. Kyle has a head for engines and machines and I took part in this conversation using knowledge that had burrowed into my head during NCT countdowns in the garage with my father. We both came from hard-working families, and we both knew that you had to earn your way through life. Kyle didn't care about school, but he had a bubbling determination in the areas of life that were important to him. I sat beside him in a woodwork class in third year, and on paper, there were no two people in the class more different than he and I. But by the measures of character... and outlook... I had never met anyone more like myself."

The Stranger listened attentively.

"They say that any friendship that lasts more than seven years will last a lifetime." "I hope you're right. But in saying that, I've learned that time means nothing when it comes to friendship. Absolutely nothing. You can connect better with someone that you met yesterday than with someone you've known for years. I clicked with Kyle instantly, and the friendship felt timeless."

"You're not wrong," he replied. "Friendship can be madness at times."

There was a brief silence, before the Stranger took me out of my thoughts, and brought me crashing back to reality.

"Do you know what's mad? I bet you didn't picture this back then; the determined pioneer that you were. You didn't think that one night you would end up sitting with a glass in your hand, telling the whole story to a stranger."

The grip tightened on my glass ever so slightly. As my thoughts ran riot, my voice cracked for a second.

"No. I never saw this coming. It's mad how fast things can change," I replied, looking at the cigarette in my hand.

I could feel the blood rushing through the veins in my head, but I held it together. Looking back up to meet the Stranger's stare, I swayed towards the argument that he was just like me; he had a warm presence to him. It was as if I was getting counselled by myself. I was so used to sitting on his side of the conversation, that I had forgotten what it was like to unload my problems.

He ventured to the table to open another bottle, patting my shoulder as he made his way past. I took a few deep breaths and composed myself.

He was right.

This was not what I had pictured. Life can send us on journeys that we never saw coming.

The Stranger sat back down and returned the cigarette to his mouth, while I laughed quietly as the novelty of the entire evening began to hit me.

"You know what? For my English mock exam, I wrote about the bicycle crash. It was so simple because it all came straight from the heart. A few days later, my teacher stopped me in the corridor and asked me if the story was true. I told him that it was and clarified his suspicions that it wasn't possible to make up a story like that. Sometimes the truth is stranger than fiction."

I sat back as I began to relax a bit more.

"I've noticed that about conversations," he replied. "It's little ones, like that one you had with a teacher, that stay with us. I forget lots of things, but I never really forget conversations."

"Words stay with us. I've realised that even sentences alone can change everything. Eric's words, for example, never left me. It's not just what someone says, it's how they say it. Advice can be hollow without a human side to it."

The Stranger nodded in agreement.

"So, what else has stayed with you? What other words haven't left that head of yours?"

I ventured back into my thoughts. Conversations and ideas bubbled to the surface. I had to explain all of this very carefully.

8

The Lighthouse Concept

I remained quiet for a few seconds.

The break between songs on the Spotify shuffle gave me the window of clear and quiet thinking that I needed, allowing me to turn to the Stranger with a plate of food for thought.

"Don't think too deep into this," I said. "Short-term, what do you want from life? In the next couple of years, for example."

The Stranger was quick to respond.

"To graduate. And to make good money as soon as possible. I've been broke for long enough."

"Yeah, that was the answer I had expected. That's your lighthouse then." "What do you mean?" he asked, as he crossed his legs.

"Your lighthouse, my friend. Your goal. Let me explain."

I took a drink and turned my focus to the ground once again.

We all have things in life that we want to achieve. We all envision a better time, when we're making more money, living more comfortably, or when we simply just feel better in ourselves. We tend to think about, 'One Day', when all these goals and desires will be fulfilled, and our actions are therefore guided by these desires. It's as if we are sailing towards a lighthouse, a distant focal point.

But remember that a lighthouse is surrounded by rock. If we met our goals and didn't have any further ambitions, we would crash, falling into a state of complacency and aimlessness.

We needn't worry, however; that will never happen. The human mind by nature is never fully satisfied, and so the lighthouse will keep moving. The glorious 'One Day' can never actually be reached, but rather it will change. When we achieve one thing in life, or reach one milestone, we will automatically think of another one. As a student, your lighthouse is your graduation. But then, when you get there, you want to find a job. Then you hunt for a pay-rise or a promotion, and so the cycle continues. This gives us a positive sense of direction, of course.

The main point, however, is that the lighthouse is more of a guidance than a destination. We often tend to get sucked into the idea of, 'I'll be happy when'. We put the 'One Day' on a pedestal, and, when we get there, it rarely lives up to how we imagined it. In a similar sense, we're often told that it's all about the journey, and not the destination.

Well let me refine that slightly; the journey never ends. There is no definitive destination. We're always going to think of something else, or something more. That's why it's important to enjoy the process in everything that you do, because the process never truly ends.

I was given a sense of how far beyond the horizon my own lighthouse was when I bought my first piece of gym equipment. They were two dumbbells, about seven kilos each. This is baby weight, and so it <u>should</u> have been. But to small Conor, it wasn't; I could hardly lift them over my head. Nevertheless, I lightened the apparatus slightly and began to build myself up as best I could.

My 'One Day' was very far away. The notion of becoming 'big Conor' almost seemed very far-fetched. But as I spent every day of the week exhausting myself until I couldn't move my arms or legs, I reminded myself of the personal promises that I had made. I believed in this vision that I had.

Around the middle of 2014, at the end of third year, things started to take shape in a sense. I was slowly getting bigger; my shoulders were showing more of a structure, and I simply felt better in myself. With this, my self-esteem improved, and I became a lot more comfortable in my own skin. In general, I was just becoming happier.

Going into transition year in school, I started my first job as a butcher. This went on to form part of my character in ways that I could never have predicted. Meeting new people, and hearing the words, 'Yes that makes sense, you look like a butcher,' was a strange concept to grasp. But anyways. This was my first peek at the real working world, and cleaning blood off walls was superb for character development, I must say.

I worked with one very distinct character; someone I will never forget, even if I tried to. His name was Keith, and he was an absolute comedian. He would tear me apart with light-hearted insults, all in the name of enjoying our time, and making the day pass as fast as possible.

But there was one thing that he always said that would truly stay with me. He would say, "Boy, you have all the knowledge in the world, but no wisdom". At the time, I laughed. I hardly even knew the difference between the two words. But over time, I would learn. I most certainly would learn.

Through Kyle, I befriended a group of great people. I felt a lot more accepted with them than I had ever felt with the people that I had grown up with. My humour and my character were far more appreciated in this new circle.

Through a cloud of exhaled smoke, the Stranger gave a silver medal interpretation.

"Good people are hard to come by," he said.

I held the cigarette between my index and middle finger and pointed it at him. "You're wrong," I replied. "Good people are easy to find, my friend. There's a simple reason. Some of the 'good people' we meet are putting on an act, covering up bitterness... hatred... jealousy, or some other underlying problem. And a lot of these 'good people' will keep their masks on, until one day, the strings break, and their true sides are revealed. The truth spills out."

I tried to select my words carefully given that this was a topic that I was passionate about, to say the least. Cautiously, I continued.

"What you mean to say is that 'good character' is hard to find. You see, good character can't be replicated, practised or performed, I suppose, for the simple reason that character manifests itself in so many intricate ways. Character is shown not just through speech and action, but also by body language and thought; it is shown through the subtle things we do. That is why the reading of character is so complex. You see, as we hunt down this Lighthouse, we will find three things without even looking for them. One of them is family. Family is not necessarily a case of blood relation as such, but rather a selected group of people that you as an individual are meant to end up with, through the power of life's delicate insistence. And within these family members, you will find character like your own. What runs parallel to this, is that when people of ill-suited character and temperament try to make their way into your close circle, negativity will be brought out within you. Unsuitable character will drain you and deprive you of any inspiration. But good character can change your mindset for the better, develop you, and drive you. The presence of good character is the most priceless commodity that we can ever ask for."

As I finished my rant, the Stranger and I had a drink. The atmosphere seemed quieter for a few seconds.

"It's amazing how people can put on an act, and cover up their true side," he said, after a few moments of thought.

"I've always admired honesty," I replied. "And my father is one man that I have to credit for that. There are no grey areas with him."

"And how were things with him at this point?"

"The pressure on our relationship was building, even more so than it had been while I was in counselling. He didn't like the concept of the gym, or any exercise really, that didn't involve a team. He felt that the nature of individuality that was involved with personal fitness, was a sign of abnormality; someone who couldn't fit in. He saw the gym work as a cry for attention, or a form of vanity. Everyone knows that we live in an age where the physicality of team sports is on the rise, so I argued this case with him, insisting that I needed to get bigger. He brushed my logical arguments aside, but I understood in a sense. His mind was closed to all of this. He saw football as a game of raw talent, and ability, neither of which I had, of course."

The Stranger was puzzled.

"But you were just trying to improve yourself; could he not see that?"

I looked at my cigarette again, preparing to unload the remainder of the royal flush to accompany the ace.

"No, my friend. There's more to it than just that. You see, what I've noticed is that, over time, an idea became planted in the minds of the generation before us. It's an idea of being 'Normal'; an unwritten set of guidelines that everyone seems to know off by heart. Chasing what you want in life and ignoring those who don't support you is not mentioned anywhere. Self-Improvement, and particularly the fitness culture I would imagine, have no residence in this 'Handbook' of being Normal. The Handbook is a set of ideals and values. It's probably held in quite high regard in most small Irish towns. In essence, you live your life and base your happiness on someone

64

else's idealised view on how we should live. Maybe it suits some people, I don't know. My father held it in quite high regard. But I knew that following these principles wasn't going to get me to where I wanted to be. So, I blatantly ignored them."

"I'm going to guess that your actions weren't taken well," he replied.

"No. Not at all. I understand in a sense. It was a culture shock. And given that only three years previously I had tried to 'starve myself', this change of tune was surely worrying. I made my reasoning clear and explained my motives. But like you say, it wasn't taken well."

I paused and continued to move my cigarette through my right hand.

"So, I had a choice. I could follow this idea of being 'Normal', and keep the peace, as they say, or do what I wanted to do and make myself happy. I chose the latter. I didn't want to disrespect my father, or everyone else who believed in the Handbook, but sometimes you have to turn your back on the people that don't support your ideas, even if they are family."

The Stranger watched my hand movements. "You still don't want a lighter, no?"

"No, hold onto it," I answered, as he retracted his outstretched hand.

I went for a refill. The ice was still somewhat fresh in the glass, which amazed me, given the heat that evening.

"You were going off and doing your own thing, I suppose."

"I was," I replied, as I sat back down. "But if I've learned anything in life, it's that our ideas will rarely be loved by everyone."

I investigated my glass for a second, before sitting forward. Another idea came to the podium; one that 'Drunk Conor' had developed over many sessions.

"Look here," I told the stranger, as I tilted the glass in his direction. "That there is a symbol of life," I said, swirling the glass.

I placed my cigarette on the arm of the chair and returned my attention to the matter at hand.

"What you're seeing there is flow. Flow is a symbol of freedom; the freedom of action and freedom of thought. If you have a job that you truly enjoy, you will never feel like you're working, because you will experience flow; the feeling of being unstoppable. People on stage, comedians, actors and actresses, singers, musicians, for example, all experience flow. In Formula One, at two hundred miles per hour, when the width of a single hair is all it takes for you to crash and burn, those gentlemen in the hot seat, experience flow. Flow is unbreakable. Flow is the greatest feeling in the world. The liquid in the glass is flow; it's freedom. It is a symbol of all the good in your life. The good character, the good thoughts, inspiration, wisdom; it's all contained in the liquid."

I lifted the glass up to our eye level and continued my analogy.

"Now, look at the ice. It moves with the flow, but it delays it, acting as an obstacle. This is all the negativity in your life. This represents the people who don't support you. This is a symbol of the things we do that we know deep down aren't good for us. This represents everything that holds us back in our pursuit of the lighthouse."

I lowered the glass and rested it on my leg.

"Finally, there's the glass itself. This is our environment, which can either be positive or negative. This can be the job we're in, or the place we live, that either enlightens us or sucks the life out of us. It all depends on how we perceive our environment. The glass can be an outright symbol of negative surroundings, toxic to our existence, or it can be the greatest support that we have. We can still experience flow whilst being trapped in a 'negative environment', hence why the liquid still moves within the glass. But say we want to change our environment, like this for example."

At that, I turned around and threw the contents of my glass out onto the concrete to my right.

"That there is chaos. We often think that running away from our problems will help us. We think that a sudden change in our environment, like going off to college or emigrating, for example, will change everything. Well, have a look over my shoulder. The environment has changed, but the flow is gone. And to add salt to wounds, the negativity is still there in all its glory. You can try to get the flow back, but much like trying to get that vodka back into the glass, it's not exactly going to be easy."

I went to the table, refilled my original glass with vodka and ice, took one of the fresh glasses that lay idle, and sat back down. Holding the two glasses out in front of us, I carefully poured the vodka from one into the other. A few of the ice cubes fell into the new glass, and some were left behind.

"But if we change our environment in a mindful and controlled manner, then we can keep our flow. Notice now how I have a fresh glass and new surroundings. By leaving the old environment, I left some negativity behind, but not all of it."

I reached into my new glass, lifted out the remaining ice cubes, and threw them to one side. Holding the glass in mid-air, I swirled it one last time.

"Now I have my flow, and the negativity is gone," I concluded, placing my glass down, and lifting the cigarette once again.

The Stranger remained silent as he digested my long-winded metaphor. I leaned forward and placed my hand on his shoulder, smiling.

"My father always taught me that experience is the best teacher, my friend."

Flow. Freedom. It's not just in a glass. It's in our minds and our hearts. We just need to find it.

9

Straight and Narrow

The Stranger was sitting quietly, processing my words. I rotated my glass on the arm of the chair and took in the scene; the muffled conversation varied in volume. Bringing my focus back to the gentleman on my left, I could see that he was still deep in thought. It was as if our roles had been reversed for a few moments; he was now the disconnected mind. I took a drink and allowed him a second to come around. Perhaps the fresh air was finally hitting him; it was hard to tell.

As he returned the cigarette to his mouth, he left his own head and came back to the present.

"What are you studying in college?" he asked, as he turned his attention back to me.

"Physics," I replied.

His facial expression changed to one of confusion and disbelief.

"Would psychology not have been a better choice for you, given your interest in behaviour, and all these ideas that you have floating around?"

I laughed, as I moved my focus to those around me.

"I chose Science for one key reason," I answered. "In maths and science, there is usually just one right answer to whatever question you are asked; there's no grey area. A numerical problem, no matter how complex, usually has only one solution. So, in terms of an exam, you either know how to figure out the answer, or you fail. Simple as that. I hated English because of its ambiguity. The way I saw it, English was a subject in which you could rightly say that two plus two is five, so long as you could prove it. I hated not knowing what the right answer was."

The Stranger perched his elbow on the arm of the chair and rested his head in his hand.

"You wanted to study something straightforward, where you knew straight away if you were right or wrong."

I nodded in agreement and turned my attention back in his direction. "Little did I know, life, in general, is much more like English than Maths. There are several right answers; and you can be guaranteed that everyone's method of getting there will be different."

I lifted my glass to take a drink but paused half-way.

"And one thing is for certain," I added. "It's never going to be straightforward."

When I was in school, Physics in NUI Galway was 450 points. Now I don't want to come across as a bit of a prick, but I had a strong sense of certainty that I would get a point score like that. Regardless of my self-assurance, I wanted to push myself.

I knew that high points could possibly line me up for a scholarship opportunity. It's no secret that college is far from cheap. I come from a good family, who would have put me through college come hell or high water, but we were by no means millionaires. As well as that, to be brutally honest, I couldn't fathom the thought of putting my hand out to the two people that raised me and saying, "Pay for those four years there, please and thanks". They had already done more than enough for me, giving me every chance that I could have possibly asked for in life and helping me through my tribulations with anorexia. I had younger siblings, and I wanted them to be a priority.

So, I took responsibility for my own scenario. I had a job that I couldn't leave, and a gym regime that I couldn't bear to give up, due to a peculiar blend of passion and fear. So, rather than wait till sixth year, and put life on hold for a while, I studied constantly for two years. I ended up sleeping about six hours a night to keep all this afloat; leaving no stone unturned, I suppose.

As cliché as this may sound, education was my ticket out. Friends of mine in college, who also come from small towns, are in the same boat. We laugh about it now. It's like in American movies; getting out of the hood, or the ghetto, or whatever it's called. I don't mean that in a condescending way, don't worry, but I had my reasons.

Like I said before about people talking; this game of Chinese Whispers. I couldn't stand it anymore. The small-town mindset was burning a hole in my happiness. On top of this, I witnessed the mythical pyramid in all of its extended glory. I learned that a village has a sort of 'bullshit hierarchy'; a few individuals who view themselves as being something more than everyone else. To this day, I have a boiling hatred for condescension, which simply stems from witnessing this circus of unjust egotism.

I had to get out.

But at the same time, you earn everything that you get. Life had gotten me out of jail twice before, so it wasn't going to give me this golden ticket without me fighting for it.

The Stranger sat forward and placed his bottle on the ground.

"Not to be abrupt, or to kill your flow or anything, but why do I get the feeling that you've said all of this before? Everything that you've said since we've sat down has sounded rehearsed to me, apart from the couple of times that you've stared across the garden and gotten a shortness of breath. I imagine that's a bit more spontaneous."

"In fairness," I replied, "I haven't had a conversation like this one. I'm normally on your side of the exchange, but I've made all of these points many times before. Come to think of it, I've said all of this both drunk and sober."

I sat forward again as my shoulders rounded over. With my eyes fixed on the concrete, I skimmed through the many conversations I'd had with people, playing the same role as the Stranger. The listener. The witness.

"When people are down and out, when they need someone to listen, you will be amazed at what they tell you. In desperate times, people will open up. I've heard stories from friends and comrades that I'm obliged to take to the grave with me."

After gathering the historical data that I needed from my repertoire of conversations, I lifted my head and faced the Stranger before I continued.

"But what's even more amazing than that is how much they listen; how much they take in. When someone needs you, and needs your help, they will listen attentively to everything you say. They will take in every word, every sentence, every anecdote. Because they understand the power of relatability. They appreciate the stories of someone in the same boat as them. They will rejoice at the fact that they are not alone. And they listen, in the hope that the next thing you say is something that they can take home with them. Something they can repeat to themselves. Something that could possibly save them. You never know who's going to be there to save you, or who you might end up saving. Always, always be mindful of how you treat people. Everyone is fighting a battle that the outside world knows nothing about."

After a heavy sigh on my behalf, the Stranger and I remained silent, taking in the scene before our eyes. The laughter around us continued, almost indefinitely.

"You know, I used to hate all this," I added, waving my hand at our surroundings.

He looked puzzled. "What do you mean?"

"All of this. The nightlife. I didn't drink till I was seventeen, and at first, I hated it. When I was in school, I would watch it all take place around me. I was so sick of it, that on a Sunday morning I would never open Snapchat. I couldn't bear to watch staged stories; the pantomime of fake people."

As the vodka meandered down through my system, I thought back to my school days for a moment.

"What really confused me… and will baffle me till the day I die, is that the people who were usually hostile with one another, for some reason, always seemed to come together when the lighting was right. It seemed as if the flash of a camera could eliminate all other matters for a split second. It was all an image, and I despised it with a passion."

The Stranger's confusion boiled over.

"What... in the name of God... happened in the meantime? You're almost half a bottle of Smirnoff in, and you're stone-cold sober. You must have embraced 'the beer' at some point."

Times had changed. Like Johnny Cash, I had to take this one piece at a time. "Oh, I did eventually, don't you worry. But at first, I tried and failed. There was something so fake about it all. It was put on, and unnecessary in my eyes."

"Do you ever feel like you missed out?" he asked, rather cautiously. I smiled and shook my head.

"FOMO is a funny feeling," I replied. "If your closest friends are all out for the night, and you're stuck at work, or studying for an exam, then yes, of course, you're going to feel like you're missing out. But following the crowd in a general sense is different."

I paused and looked around again.

"You don't need to be a detective to know what's going on in the bathroom upstairs at the minute, so let me use cocaine as an example. We're probably the only two here tonight who aren't taking it, besides Ciaran over there; he's too busy talking. Why do a lot of us take drugs in the first place? To not miss out on the experience, or because everyone else is doing it. I've tried myself on a couple of occasions, although it isn't for me, I must say. I'll stick to the vodka. But most of those around us tonight are completely oblivious to the conversation that you and I are having. They've hardly even noticed us all evening. Given the nature of what you and I are saying, we might mention something that one of them really needs to hear; a split second of unintentional eavesdropping could give someone here the encouragement to get something off of *their* chest. My point is this. What I've found over time is that following everyone else can take you away from what's important. Following the crowd can distract you from becoming the person that you're meant to be. If I had drunk my late teens away, like most of those around me at the time, I wouldn't be the athlete that I am now. Or an even more sinister thought, I might not have gotten enough points to come to Galway. Being true to yourself is difficult, but it will always be worth it. By following everyone else in an attempt to 'not miss out', you may end up missing out on the things that are most important to you."

The Stranger slowly nodded in agreement.

"Fair enough," he replied. "I never thought of it like that."

He took a drag on his cigarette and paused for a moment. "Speaking of being an athlete, how was 'getting big' going?" he asked.

I smiled, thinking back, as my eyes moved towards the ground again.

"By the time I was seventeen, I didn't know myself. It's weird how things change. I started to climb the ranks in this make-believe pyramid, not that I cared about that anyway. Many of the sly remarks and piss-takes ground to a halt, and many of my mouthy peers had become a lot quieter in our old age. I was becoming more respected, and there was even the odd enquiry as to how I was making such good progress. There's a glorious little phrase; 'Never pick on little boys, because they always grow up'."

The Stranger smiled.

"Everything was falling into place?"

"In a sense, yes. Everything was lining up nicely... but there was still one more change that I had to make. A change that would... completely detach me from this ideal view of... of being Normal."

10

Just Be Normal

According to the dictionary, 'normal' can mean conforming to a standard, being typical, usual and expected. So, what's expected of you at sixteen and seventeen? From what I could see, looking out through the lenses of what felt like heightened maturity, that I couldn't yet categorise as a blessing or a curse, I noticed two things. The first was a desire to fit in, and to be liked and admired. The second aspect I noticed was a love for living in the moment; not thinking about tomorrow, forgetting yesterday, but still not being fully focused on today. A sense of being lost in the now, taking every few seconds as they come, without designating any real purpose to the time you have.

Between being myself and thinking about the long run, I was supposedly far from this definition. By the laws of the Handbook, I was an outcast. But there was one delicate string still tying me to this sacred unwritten scripture; an element of life that had caused me more pain than joy. An element of life that had to go.

Around the Easter of 2016, I was playing for the senior team, but not getting much game time. We had a friendly against a neighbouring club, and I arrived at half-time, coming straight from work. After taking a jersey from the dressing room, probably number twenty-nine, I arrived pitch-side. Given very delicate instructions, despite the game being long lost, I was sent in as corner-forward.

For much of the game, the ball never left our own half. Amidst the heavy downfall of rain that evening, I stood there in deep thought.

Was this it?

Was this what I had poured years of my young life into?

To stand here like a fool, and play a game that suits someone else's idealised vision of what life is, and should be, all about?

Two passes came my way in the space of twenty minutes, both of which I misjudged, losing possession in seconds. Like I said, I could never read the game. I looked to the stands on the far side-line, seeing the people who only ever knew me as a substitute, a back-up, and a replacement. I couldn't keep this up, living in the shadows of others around me. To some of my teammates on the green grass that day, I was still only the runt of the litter. One of the hardest things to accept in life is that you will never change in the eyes of some people.

The final whistle blew on that cold April evening. As we walked to the dug-out, handshakes were exchanged with our opponents. The managerial congress spoke a few words of wisdom about our performance, but I wasn't listening. We made our way up the grass towards the clubhouse, as a team-mate of mine turned to me. "What did you think of that?" he asked me. I left my jersey on the table in the centre of the dressing room and turned to him. "Fuck this," I said, as I threw on a jacket. And I walked out. Young dreams of the county panel, which realistically were long dead, were now properly buried. There was an element of sadness, but only for a moment.

In those few seconds, I realised that I would never again be at the bottom of the food chain. I would never again be the runt of the litter. I was taking the cubes of ice out of the glass one by one. And the flow would come. Over time, the flow would come.

A few weeks later, my father questioned my absences at training; word had gotten back to him that I was nowhere to be seen on a Friday evening. I turned to him and broke the news that I'd gotten fed up. He asked if I would continue going to the gym, given that there was no real need anymore.

I froze on the spot.

I no longer had an excuse to justify the part of my life that he, among others, viewed as the cherry on the cake of my 'abnormality'. I pointed out to him that it was something I enjoyed, and that I wasn't going to stop.

He didn't speak for a few seconds. Upon gathering his thoughts, he gave his opinion, heavily influenced by the Handbook. But I had stopped listening. The decision I had made in 2014 to choose my goals and stay true to myself, had been like a free trial. This particular day was where the official subscription would start. I had completely turned my back on this sacred idea of being normal.

The Stranger was silent as I kept my focus on the cigarette in my hand.

"I suppose it happens," he said quietly. "A teenager falling out with his father." I pointed my cigarette at him and cut the brief silence.

"In fairness to him," I replied, "since I left home and moved to Galway, some peace and mutual respect have been restored. But I don't blame him one bit for what happened at the time. He's set in his ways, like most men. You must accept that some people aren't going to fully agree with what you do with yourself. It's a huge part of life. Never be bitter about that. It's bad for your heart, such negative energy."

I finished my drink and turned back to the Stranger.

"You'll have another," I said, telling him rather than asking. "Thank you."

I made my way to the table and threw him another bottle, before refilling my own glass.

The Stranger was right.

I was half a bottle of Smirnoff deep into our conversation. At this point, I'd usually be slurring, and making little to no sense, but I was stone-cold sober. My senses were heightened, it seemed; my heart was beating at the usual pace, but it was very prominent. I could feel it in unexpected places, like in my lower arm, and down my jaw. Now, perhaps I was hallucinating. It could have been dehydration or the heat of the evening. I'll never know. Within the intensity of conversation, I was feeling slightly numb in a sense.

Anyway, I had to stop conversing with my own faint reflection in the kitchen window and return to my seat.

As I sat down, my facial expression communicated the fact that I had something to say but couldn't quite find the words, so the Stranger allowed me time for this mental buffering.

"In 2016, I went to this... academic summer camp thing," I said. "It was where the crème de la crème of young intelligence came together, supposedly. You think you're smart until you attend something like that. These young people were incredible. But in those two weeks, I learned more about life than I did about science. I met a few great people, but I didn't really fit in there, to be honest. After three days, I couldn't wait to get home and talk nonsense with Kyle and the rest of the lads. There's only so much 'intellectual conversation' you can handle in a fortnight."

I sat forward slightly and concentrated on the scene in my head.

"But I'll never forget on the last day, seeing people in tears, as the tragic truth dawned on me. For fifty weeks of the year, many of these people were victims of the Handbook; unable to live up to the narrow-minded expectations of an ignorant society. But for those twelve days in July, they could be themselves. For twelve days, they didn't have to think about the opinions of others. The idea of being normal vanished into thin air."

The Stranger digested my words with patience and unrivalled understanding. "It's almost like a stigma."

"It was inspiring in a sense," I replied, after a brief silence. "It was a message to me to keep being myself. If I could hold my head up high all year round, the way that these people could for twelve days, then I would be a very happy man."

"So, without football, what were you going to do?" he asked, lighting another cigarette.

I sat back again and rested my head on the top of the chair.

"I started watching YouTube constantly. In a couple of months, I had probably watched every World's Strongest Man final of the previous twenty years. I was moved by power; uplifted by what people were capable of. Arnold Schwarzenegger once said that no matter how civilised we became as humans, we always admired power. It's genetic; it's wired into us. It's a respect and a desire that we can't disown. No matter how uninterested a man may seem in his physical capabilities, watch when one of his peers... his comrades... challenges him to something as simple as an arm-wrestle. Watch how his body language changes. You will see a spike in confidence, and a side of ego that might not have been present before. Strength is a universal language... and it may be physical, emotional, or spiritual, but regardless, it is respected."

I took a deep breath. The shoes of my seventeen-year-old self walked a mountainous terrain of ignored opinions and spiritual setbacks, so retracing those steps was proving difficult.

"So, I thought back to the promises I had made to myself, at thirteen and fourteen, to never be weak again. Perhaps I could go a bit further. I was seventeen, with no knowledge of the sport of powerlifting, or bodybuilding, or anything like that. But I made another blind promise... I moved the lighthouse way off into the distance, beyond any perceivable horizon. My typical thought to myself has always been, 'God, could you imagine?', thinking to myself about crazy things like being a millionaire, or having a garage full of every car I ever thought of driving. Something I would say when an idea seemed unattainable. And I said those words... Could I imagine myself on a powerlifting stage? Could I picture a few hundred kilos on my back, or in my hands? And the mad thing is that I could... I honestly thought of how crazy it would be, to shock people with a certain level of strength, and to be able to turn around and say that I was once on the verge of dying from being too small. It would be personal proof that you can change your life if you really, really want to."

The Stranger paused for a moment to take in the absolute mouthful that I had landed upon him.

"You were aiming high." "I was."

He rotated the bottle in his hands, as a sense of concern drifted into the conversation.

"Had football not scared you away from aiming so high so soon, given how it fell to pieces? Were you not setting yourself up for disappointment all over again?"

He hit a nerve.

A flashback came and went in those seconds, as laughter echoed through my head, although much more intense this time. The sour tequila shot of failure coated the inside of my mouth, so I had no choice but to bite down hard on whatever slice of optimism I could find.

"There's something funny that I've realised," I coldly explained. "If you're good at something, people will applaud you. Maybe you're a great footballer, or a great

83

musician perhaps. People applaud talent and hard work...
but the minute you express ambition, you're considered
an idiot. Aiming high, and ambition in general, is mocked
and laughed at, picked apart and torn down... and that's
what makes aiming high so addictive. There is a peculiar
sense of fulfilment in proving wrong the people who gave
you no chance; no ounce of faith or belief."

The Stranger didn't say a word, so I cut the silence.

"I understand your argument, my friend, and you're not
wrong. I *had* failed miserably before. But I was going to
aim high and if I fell short, I'd still be a long way off my frail
and fragile past self. This was more than just a sport. This
was running away from who I used to be."

11

Realisations

Darkness was falling. With everyone else getting that little bit more drunk by the minute, the Stranger and I were sobered by our conversation, our words perfectly cancelling the effect of every mouthful.

I heard a burst of audacious laughter coming from across the patio. Ciaran was by the speaker still, bottle in hand, chatting to another good friend of ours. I was happy to see them in such good spirits, but I thought nothing more of the situation. The Stranger, however, had other ideas.

"He's a real chandelier in the room, that fella. He's the only voice that I've been able to distinguish from the noise all evening."

I fully agreed.

"It's not even a case of him being loud," I replied. "He's just a real presence in the room. And God bless him, he has no shortage of confidence."

The Stranger turned his attention back to me. "And what about you? Are you like that?"

My eyes met the concrete again, as I remembered the first conversations that I had had with Ciaran. Times change, as do people, but some truths will remain.

"I often end up as the centre of attention. I often put a friend over my head on a night out or something like that. But the funny thing is I never intend for it to happen. Some people, like myself and Ciaran, and countless others I've met, just have a presence to us it seems; an ability to light up the room."

Wow, the arrogance of that statement. I assumed in the moment that the Stranger would judge me, but after my split second of panic, I remembered the genuine and open-minded nature of the gentleman sitting beside me.

"Natural entertainers. Everyone needs that. You need a bit of life in the room, no matter where you are, or how formal the evening is," he said, smiling.

I sat forward, facing the ground once again, with my arms resting on my thighs.

"It's more than just the idea of being entertaining. It takes a certain type of person to bring such energy and 'buzz' to an environment, without coming across as attention-seeking, or, for the want of better words, a loud prick. I realised over time that most of the natural comedians I ever came across had a few common traits. Myself included. A sort of common denominator."

"And what was it?"

I paused for a moment before lifting my head out of the concrete daze.

"We knew what it felt like to be truly unhappy. It was as if we made the room laugh so that no-one else would feel the pain that we had felt."

The Stranger nodded in reply, as he took a drag on his cigarette.

"I get that," he said. "I'm not one for taking over the room, but I never want anyone to feel unhappy. That's why I do this. I listen to people who need to talk. That's my contribution."

I smiled. It's a small world. This man was just like me; a listener who would appear out of nowhere when you needed him, with open ears and an open mind. Character always appears at the right moment.

"So," he said, removing the ash from his cigarette, and sitting back. "In saying that, I better keep listening. Carry on."

I nodded, took a drink, and delved back into my memories.

Giving up football and focusing solely on just the gym, meant that I was getting stronger at an appreciable rate. By seventeen, I was bench-pressing over a hundred kilos, and lifting the guts of two hundred kilos from the floor. I felt like an animal, and this worked wonders for my self-esteem. I finally felt like I was good at something that I truly cared about.

The stress release of the gym was needed more than ever, as sixth year proved itself to be just as difficult and draining as I had expected it to be. It was the epitome of the Lighthouse Concept; constantly striving for the 'One Day' when life would get better.

However, there were a couple of entities outside of school that made life that little bit easier and made 'the process' that bit more enjoyable. One of them was the fact that Kyle, or 'Clive', had become more like a brother to me than a friend. He really is one of the family that life has given me.

Looking back, I've come to a realisation. People will tell you that school is completely different to the outside world, and they would be right. But a message like that will have trouble nesting itself in your subconscious when you're being led to believe that points and courses are your only option, and that you might as well blow the final whistle on your hopes if you can't perform in those overwhelming two weeks in June.

I had a brilliant maths teacher in fifth and sixth year. She had a gift for communicating, and a way of simplifying the mind fuck that is honours maths. But she always said the word 'June'. Life revolved around June. I can't blame her; no-one can. This was the tunnel vision that she was obliged to instil in us; this was the system that we were a part of.

The month of June was supposedly going to define the rest of our lives. If this idea held water, then I was going to have a life of smooth sailing; on the other hand, my dear friend Kyle was in a serious pickle. He won't mind me saying this, but he can't spell the word 'degree'. Keith's concept regarding the almighty difference between knowledge and wisdom was going to prove itself over time.

Now, I wasn't completely stupid. I knew the value of common sense, the importance of things like communication, and other skills that you pick up when your head isn't buried in a textbook. But I was ignorant of the power of these things. I was simply ignorant of the fact that wisdom could build a life just as well, if not better than knowledge ever could.

Years of watching "Top Gear" had given me the basis for an idea along these same lines. There's a famous racetrack in Germany called 'The Nürburgring'. For young petrol-heads, it's essentially the equivalent to Wembley Stadium, or Wimbledon, and throughout its lifetime, it has taken several lives. Its sharp corners, combined with what I can only imagine to be the subconscious pressure of knowing that you are on one of the most prestigious pieces of asphalt in the world, makes the experience a very challenging one.

Now, in a light-hearted contrast, there is a song called, "Life is a Highway". What I found in school was that we were force-fed a message like that. Life is a highway or a motorway, a straight-line drag race against poverty and failure, with good grades and a degree being viewed as the acceleration off the start line. I found that we were instilled with a sense of entitlement. Given the fact that I was always academic, I was led to believe that the highway of life would serve me well, and that I was owed something.

But here's a key insight; a take-home point. Life owes you fuck all. The linear motorway, which we all feel entitled to be on, where simply driving faster will get you to your destination sooner, is a myth. Life is more like the Nürburgring; a winding route where you really don't know what's coming next.

Whilst taking this route, it sinks in that the ground you're on has taken many lives before, and that it's not going to think twice about taking yours either. Only sheer focus and determination can keep you away from *crashing. Life is the same. But crashing in life, just like on the track, is not the be-all and end-all. It's more like a lesson; a reminder to not make the same mistake, and perhaps to brake earlier the next time you encounter that same corner.*

But more importantly, remember this. The Nürburgring has hosted some of the greatest races of all time. It's only natural that every driver that ventures onto it, whether it be on race day, or just at his or her own leisure, feels a certain sense of gratitude.

When we picture life as the motorway, we feel that we deserve to go places, and that it must be simple. When we eventually see life as the treacherous racetrack that it is, we suddenly realise that we are lucky to be alive; that we need to be grateful for the fact that we can still prove ourselves. We become grateful for the fact that we still have a chance.

I sat back for a second.

The talk of gratitude widened my eyes for a few moments. I was very grateful, especially for the people around me. But in essence, I was just grateful to be alive.

I turned my focus back to the Stranger; the gentleman was in deep thought, brewing a response. As he placed his bottle on the ground, he remained hunched forward with his arms resting on his legs and his hands clasped.

"I know the feeling. We think that life's going to be simple just because a piece of paper says so. The naivety of it all is madness."

I nodded and laughed quietly.

Resting my glass on the arm of the chair, I turned my gaze to the top of the wall directly across from me. Ideas were racing back and forth in my mind.

"The wisest person I have ever met is a woman called Deniese," I said, pausing for a second, and filtering through the endless wisdom that this amazing woman had portrayed in all the times I had met her. I had to get my words right. It would be a sin to recall Deniese's lessons without proper execution.

"There's one particular ace card in the precious deck of thoughts that she shared. She said that everything we do, we do because of one of these two motives. Love, and Fear... It hit me; how simple it is. Then I thought about it and broke it down for myself. These two motives often work hand in hand. When you're in school, you're probably motivated by fear... a fear of not getting enough points. Then, when you're in college, you're motivated either by the love of what you're studying, or the love of the salary you may end up on. And if that love isn't strong enough, then you drop out. Now, you find yourself motivated by fear once again, the fear of being broke, to either find something more interesting to study, or to find the best possible job that doesn't require a degree. When you're young, and you're working behind a bar, or as a waiter or waitress, your most probable motive is a fear of having no money, or a fear of not acquiring enough money. But fast forward, maybe ten or fifteen years, when you're hopefully qualified or promoted, or more experienced, the best possible scenario is that you're in a position that you love, and you're motivated by the enjoyment and the sense of fulfilment that your work brings you. Then, I related the idea to myself."

Again, like Johnny Cash, it was a case of one piece at a time as I waded through a harsh memory or two.

"When I began lifting weights, my actions were motivated by a fear of being too small; a fear of being bullied, and disrespected... Fast forward a couple of years, and my motivation is now... mainly... the love of being strong."

My right hand trembled slightly. Laughter came and went, somewhere in the darkest corner of my subconscious. I composed myself, swallowed hard, and gathered my thoughts.

"It became clear to me that many of the things we do in life are motivated by fear; a fear of impending regret, a fear of missing out on an opportunity, or a fear of remaining in a state of unhappiness. And the greatest outcome we can hope for is that through progress over time, the fear will slowly decay, and that we can continue these same endeavours, motivated by the love we have for them."

I paused and turned my attention back to the Stranger.

"They reckon love is the most powerful emotion, and that it brings out a side of people that they didn't even know they had. Well, whoever said that... did not have a clue about fear."

After taking a drink, I lowered the empty glass and held the vodka in my mouth for a few seconds. As I rested my head back, I felt the subtle burning sensation in my chest. The Stranger said nothing and allowed me a second or two to come to terms with my own words.

"You've talked a lot about fear since we've sat down," he said. "But when someone is in their own head, especially when they're drunk, there's a good chance that love is involved. I can't tell you how many times I've sat like this with heartbroken friends."

I laughed quietly as I made a brief analysis of what was happening at that very second. I was pouring my past out to this man that I had just met, and now he was pulling strings to make sure I kept talking.

In fairness to him, sometimes that kind of encouragement is needed.

"Fair enough, you're not wrong," I replied. "I met a girl when I was in sixth year. We were together for over a year before things fell to pieces."

The Stranger smirked.

"I knew well. We all have our demons, but heartbreak is one thing that really cracks a person. It's crazy how someone else can dominate our emotions."

"You're absolutely right," I replied. "But heartbreak isn't the only problem. It's the side effects of it all that can really tear you apart. When the dust settles, and you're left with the thoughts of 'what if?', along with the odd feeling of not being good enough perhaps, then it's those thoughts and emotions that can mentally tear you limb from limb."

Heartbreak is awful, we all know that, and it's inevitable for most of us. Heartbreak was one of the corner-pieces of the jigsaw of my ideas that I was trying to recreate in front of the Stranger's eager eyes. It said 'twenty years' on the box, but I had to try and form it in a couple of hours. I was on a chronological roll, and I had to keep the momentum going before the vodka in my system could hit me.

"I'll come back to that in a minute or two," I said. "But before I do, I have an idea that I want to share with you."

The Stranger ushered me to continue. He seemed to be in his element, just listening. My eyes turned towards the ground again, as I gathered my wandering thoughts.

12

Opportunities and Obstacles

In my time, I've had three, how can I put this, significant... individual ideas, or personal goals. These three goals lead me to the formation of an idea in my head, regarding opportunity. I realised that, much like employers advertising positions, life advertises opportunities in the same way.

In order to qualify for these opportunities, life has what I call, 'the three criteria'. When you pursue something, you need to show life that you have three things: an idea, a plan, and a belief. The first two are quite simple, although the third one is much more complex.

Self-belief, although it is always talked about and promoted, is a rare commodity. They say common sense isn't that common; well self-belief rarely comes from within oneself. It's usually prompted or ignited by an external source, an encouragement, a moment of inspiration, or a statement. But like I said before, about fulfilment being the achievement and acquisition of your inner desires, when self-belief does start within oneself, then it is far more powerful. It's like the idea that you will never forget the things that you teach yourself.

Goal number one of three was to put myself through college without placing any financial pressure on my family. The events of June 2017 had served me well, with the leaving cert going as smoothly as I could have hoped. So, in September 2017, I received an offer for the All-Ireland Scholarship, sponsored by the multi-millionaire, JP McManus. The scholarship removed a huge weight of financial worry, and for that I was, and still am of course, eternally grateful. This opportunity took me to Galway, releasing me from the small-town shenanigans that I had grown so hateful of.

Goal number two was, like I said before, to 'never be weak again'. I wanted to become a good powerlifter, or strength athlete in general, I suppose. Two days after receiving the scholarship, I stepped on a powerlifting stage for the first time. I was greeted with a standing ovation, from men twice my size, when I bench-pressed 135 kilos at eighteen years old. Hours upon hours spent alone in a bedroom, and a few hundred euros invested in equipment had paid off. Memories of being left on a side-line, and being too small to run, walk, or even breathe, were dismissed for a brief moment.

But my knowledge of the sport was still limited, and this would eventually stall my progress if I didn't seek experienced help. A conversation with a stranger beside a squat rack in the Kingfisher Gym in NUIG led to me becoming a member of Galway Powerlifting Club. With great coaching, and a welcoming team around me, I now had what I needed to fulfil any potential I had of becoming the strongest possible version of myself.

In the space of a couple of months, life had handed me two invaluable opportunities. This was proof to me that

anything I wanted from life, within logical reasoning, was
possible, provided I believed in my goals, and in myself.

"You said it yourself. You always looked ahead and left no stone unturned." I paused for a second and sighed heavily.

"We can all set goals. We can all chase our ambitions and follow the lighthouse. But you can't plan everything. You never know what life is going to hit you with. The water that we sail on is… is prone to tidal waves and choppy conditions. The process is, to quote friends of mine, 'just never simple'."

As I sat further back into the chair, and further back into myself, the Stranger started putting the pieces together.

"The belief that life is a highway caught you off guard. You thought that it would all be simple when you came to college; that it would all fall into place."

I nodded in agreement and focused my eyes on the ground again. "When everything was going well, life began to test me," I answered, swallowing hard. "It tested me through fear." I felt different in those few seconds.

I felt numb.

My mind flashed back to sitting in Corrib Village, alone, with my head in my hands, wondering what was wrong with me. I was going into dark territory.

There's a negative phrase that I've picked up over time - 'It would just be my luck' - an insinuation that we are only deserving of bad fortune. It's a phrase that leads us to accept negativity with open arms and renders us shocked when anything actually goes our way. This phrase managed to nest itself somewhere in my mind and stayed there rent-free.

So, as I went about college life in Galway, it felt as if everything was too good to be true. I didn't know how to deal with good fortune; I suppose I had gotten used to fighting a battle with my back against the wall. And with more time on my hands to think about things, my mind started playing games with me. It was almost like imposter syndrome; I didn't feel worthy of what I had gained.

There is a phenomenon known as intrusive thoughts. To my knowledge, it's one of the four branches of OCD. These thoughts are described as unwanted impulses or mental images that often cause anxiety, stress and an inability to function. Now, I didn't diagnose myself as being OCD. But looking back, I can relate to this feeling.

These thoughts were spurred on by a fear of going backwards, and these 'voices' convinced me that one wrong move would ruin everything; that one mistake would take away my position in college and send me home in disgrace. This idea of, 'what if?', rattled my mind.

What if something happened to the apartment? What if I left the oven on and caused a fire?

What if I left a tap running and flooded the place?

These are all preposterous questions, and the likelihood of a running tap flooding a five-room apartment is relatively slim.

But these thoughts would never leave. What if I didn't submit an assignment properly, and failed a module?

What if I missed a lecture, by sleeping in perhaps, and my attendance was deemed unsatisfactory? I became trapped in my own head, paranoid that I would do something that would throw this chance that I had been given, out the window.

When I was with a crowd, I was fine. In lectures, or in the gym, I was perfect; my usual vibrant self. I was proving to myself my own concept of the comedian denominator. I could light up a room, but when nightfall came and I found myself alone, the demons came out to play. These thoughts manifested further, leading me to other preposterous conclusions, even making me feel insecure in my relationship, for no apparent reason.

I didn't know how to handle it.

This was my first real battle with my own mind since overcoming anorexia. It had been so long since I had been in the cage. The Monkey had cousins who specialised in different areas of the mind. He must have informed them of where the gap was in the fence.

My biggest mistake was that I never really spoke about this to anyone at the time. I felt pathetic, and almost guilty. I convinced myself that having time to think was the issue. If I had more to worry about, perhaps if I were doing a harder course, or working more hours at the weekend, then maybe I wouldn't have this problem. I was telling myself all the wrong things.

The gym was my greatest escape from this mental turmoil, but the voices learned how to get around that. They wouldn't bother me until I was at my most vulnerable.

First thing in the morning, and last thing at night were my two biggest obstacles, when I had no phone in my hand, and my mind could take over.

After about two months, I had an idea. I concluded that if I couldn't hear these voices, then they wouldn't be a problem. So, I started listening to music twenty-four seven. Even in lectures, I would have one earphone in. I even resorted to listening to the radio through different apps.

Anything to avoid silence.

This probably wasn't the best way to deal with the problem, but it worked. I became more relaxed. It sank in that I had earned the right to be in college, and that life wasn't going to burn me at the stake for missing a lecture. Common sense and logical thinking hopped back into the driver's seat and told the voices where to go.

I was drifting in and out of the conversation, getting lost in my thoughts.

"It's mad how your mind can play games with you," he said. "For everything to go wrong within, when it's going so well externally."

I moved the cigarette through my fingers again. The Stranger didn't realise how relevant that sentence would be. He was casting the spotlight on what I can only describe as a lingering theme for the recent future of my recollections. "What I thought was a gentle corner, turned out to be a hairpin. You learn through experience," I replied.

I glanced at my empty glass.

Best to wait a minute. I needed to be as sober as possible to recall these next few memories.

The Stranger didn't say a word for a few seconds, and in the brief local silence, I could feel my heart beating on the side of my head.

"I re-found some small sense of direction as the clock turned to 2018, and I had planned to compete again on the May bank holiday weekend. With a new team around me and brilliant coaching, powerlifting felt like less of an individual effort, and more like a team sport, giving me a great sense of belonging."

"One that football never gave you," he replied, smiling.

"Exactly," I said, with a deflating sigh. "The second semester of college was starting, and I had befriended a few... invaluable people by this stage. I talk a lot about family, and this handful are no exception. Character always comes at the right time. Life presents people to us at the most random of moments. The strangest story I can tell you is how I met a guy called Finley. We sat talking one night, for a solid hour, in a laundromat in Corrib Village, and from that moment on a friendship was born... Life can be cruel and will present you with tough times. But what I have found is that it will also equip you for these moments... Your survival kit for your tough times is going to be the people that you hold dearest."

I paused for a moment, and with a split-second smile, I internally saluted those who meant the world to me.

"With the financial burden of college lifted off the shoulders of my family and me, I decided to learn how to drive, and pump whatever savings I had into my first car.

All these individual things gave me a sense of direction; the pursuit of the lighthouse kept me in good spirits."

The Stranger listened carefully.

"It sounds like things were improving. You had settled in, and you felt a bit more at home," he said, before venturing towards the table to take another bottle. He removed the lid with his lighter and sat back down.

I was breathing very slowly, treading carefully on the tightrope of my thoughts, somewhere between the present and the past.

"Everything was good, for a few weeks, anyway. I had found my footing, as you say. I had settled in and was much happier. Then something... quite... disturbing happened. Something that, initially, I took no notice of, but in hindsight, this thought scares me."

I sat forward and fixed my vision on the glass in my hand.

"I'm a huge fan of Steve Harvey. He once talked about a quote from Albert Einstein. Einstein supposedly once said that our imagination is a preview to life's coming attractions. In essence, the things we imagine can very well happen. It's a very hopeful, and positive thought. If you can see it in your head, then there is no reason why it can't become a reality. This is great when you're on the subject of ambition and goals."

I paused for a moment, as I took a deep breath.

"At the Corrib Village initiation meeting in the September of first year, we were told to be vigilant if we ever saw someone walking along the Corrib river at night; there was a chance that the person in question may be in a bad place mentally. I can't remember the advice we were given, whether it was to go up and talk to them, to leave them be, or to call for help; I can't remember. Ironically. But we were presented with the scenario; food for thought, I suppose. About a month into the second semester, a conversation with my girlfriend regarding college choices and future plans changed the game very suddenly, and put an expiry date as such on our relationship."

I went quiet for a few seconds, so the Stranger took advantage of the opportunity to intervene.

"These things happen. Especially when you're young. Like you say, it's never straightforward."

I shook my head, and slowly gathered the words that I needed.

"I know these things happen, my friend. That wasn't the problem. When this conversation was taking place, a vision flashed into my head, without me thinking. You probably won't even believe this. I could see myself, for some reason, staggering on the path beside the Corrib river, with a bottle in my hand. It was like a fucked-up prophecy of what was to come. In hindsight, it was a sign; it was life telling me that the keys to my happiness were slowly falling into someone else's pocket."

My hands were shaking slightly as I spoke, and I could feel my chest tighten. The Stranger didn't flinch.

"Like many fellas before you, you were wrapped around a girl's finger," he replied.

He had a point. I've learned that love is a blinding set of headlights, but it's up to you to make sure you stay on your side of the road.

The patio behind the Stranger and I was a blanket of darkness. As the conversation around us ceased for a moment, everything went relatively quiet. I'm a huge fan of the Arctic Monkeys, and the brief silence between songs was broken by the well-known, 'R U Mine'.

The lyrics that I had sung on so many occasions, whilst being in another stratosphere of inebriation, were a bitter pill to swallow at that very moment, laden with relevant irony. I slowly rotated the glass about its axis on the left arm of the chair, and my vision focused itself on the wall across the patio.

"I firmly believe that self-respect is important in any relationship, friendship, or any bond at all," I said. "Everyone has the right to set a standard for their partner, or for those around them, as to how they wish to be treated. So, one night, when presented with an ultimatum as such, I agreed to give up powerlifting in order to make my relationship a priority. I agreed that May fifth would be the last powerlifting meet that I would do, and that from then on, I would invest more time and energy into making the relationship work."

The Stranger remained silent.

I swallowed hard as laughter shot through my subconscious. My grip tightened on my glass, so much so that to this day I don't know how it didn't crack.

"For a moment, I forgot what had saved me as a teenager. I forgot what had stopped the piss-taking and disrespect. I forgot about the promises that I had made to myself."

I turned my gaze back towards the Stranger.

104

"Sacrifice is important," I added. "Give and take is important. But never give up who you are. For anybody. Your personal identity is the one thing no-one can ever take from you. So, the last thing you ought to be doing is throwing it away."

There was a brief silence, as I turned my focus back towards the ground. "Whether you want to admit it or not," he replied, "love brought out a side of you that you didn't know you had."

I sighed heavily.

"Maybe it did. But about a month later, the relationship fell apart. I called it off in a very immature fashion, and to say that I didn't handle it well would be an understatement. The thought of hurting anybody rattles my insides, so guilt played me like a fiddle in the weeks after. We all make mistakes, I suppose."

"Don't beat yourself up. You're not the first person to end on bad terms, and you won't be the last."

I nodded, although it was a delayed reaction, it must be said.

"I was... bitterly engrossed, to say the least, consumed by the thoughts of all the good times that I could have had, and the people I could have met if I had gone out a bit more during my first year, and if I hadn't been so cautious about giving my ex any reason to be insecure. It was my first and only real experience with FOMO. But there was no point crying over spilt milk at that stage."

My mind tiptoed forward a couple of weeks, to the May bank holiday weekend.

"After a few weeks of being pretty fucking confused and heart-broken, a 225-kilo deadlift in front of a crowd in Galway may well have saved everything; a   reminder of what I held dear to my heart."

I stopped dead in the tracks of my thoughts. I smiled as I recalled the jubilation of that moment, and the pride that I felt in those few seconds. But with the snap of life's fingers, I fell back into the reality of the present.

I rotated the empty glass once more, and then removed my hand. Everything stood still, and to me, everything went quiet.

"But then I came home for the summer. The dust settled. Everything, and I mean everything, sank in."

I swallowed hard, trying to overcome the lump in my throat.

"The demons of my first year of college woke up their dormant ancestors. There's no other way to put it."

I placed the cigarette down on the arm of the chair. Sometimes you forget the severity of certain elements of your past. When you least expect it, they can hit you like a brick wall. I got up from my seat and made my way into the house.

As I passed familiar, smiling faces, I ventured further into myself. My breathing began to speed up as I made my way through the downstairs hallway. The bathroom was at the top of the stairs, and I pretty much fell in the door.

Someone had left the light on. We can call that a faint symbol of hope, but there's no point being dramatic at this stage.

13

The Crack

The evening's recollection of one or two traumatic memories had turned my stomach, leaving me on my knees with my arms wrapped around the toilet bowl and vomiting profusely. Dizzy, and very unsteady, I slowly got to my feet. I turned to my right and was met in the mirror by my frightening reflection. My eyes were bloodshot beyond belief, and watering heavily. The veins were bulging on the side of my head, and I was as white as the sink which I had no choice but to cling onto for balance. For a moment, I could see the malnourished ghost of my past; a frail and fragile being, hiding under the mirage of character that I had formed in the years since we last spoke. I was breathing heavily, physically and mentally drained.

My mind traced back to that deadlift on May fifth. As I dropped the bar to the ground that day, my mental barriers dropped with it. The memorable applause of a hundred people was drowned out by laughter, as I returned to my thousand-yard stare at my own reflection. My stomach turned further.

In the moment, I remembered all the ideas that I had presented to the Stranger throughout the evening. I was far from finished. I had a lot more 'rehearsed wisdom' to share with him. So, as the remaining ideas formed an orderly and chronological queue in my mind, a few cards fell out of the deck; dark realisations from my darkest hours.

As I looked in the mirror, a bitter realisation approached the podium in my mind. I call it, 'The Avicii Concept'.

Avicii once asked that we wake him up when it's all over. I know it was Aloe Blacc who sang that song but bear with me. Excessive sleeping is supposedly a sign of depression, a brief escape from an inadequate reality. Avicii took his own life in April 2018. Around that time, I started working in a bar.

A few weeks after his death, the matter was being dissected among the locals. Avicii died with a net worth of roughly fifty million dollars, a gingerbread trail of successful albums and singles, and a significant impact left on the culture of music and entertainment as we know it. As I pulled a pint of Heineken, the regulars behind me questioned how a man so wealthy could possibly fall into a state of unhappiness so detrimental, that he would feel the urge to take his own life. Contrary to the usual set-up, the taps were at the back of the bar, so my back was turned to the crowd. I stood quietly and said to myself, "I get it. I know why he did it."

Now, I'm not comparing myself to one of the most successful people of the modern era, but there was an opportunity for relatability. Twelve months previously, I had prayed for a financial break-through to get me through college. I had prayed for my own car, my own independence, and to meet new people. I had prayed for success on a powerlifting stage, and an opportunity to better myself in the sport. There I stood, twelve months later, blessed with everything that I had asked for, and in the worst mental state of my life.

News of my sporting endeavours had reached home via Facebook, and people raised a glass to me in the bar, in respect of my efforts.

I put on a brave face.

As I placed a pint of Guinness in front of a former classmate of my mother's, he informally interrogated me about life in Galway. I imagine this happens to a lot of young people who come home from the big city for the summer. Questions about exams, career plans, nights out, women, and whatever else crosses the mind of the curious customer. When I told this man that I had passed my exams, recently lifted the guts of five hundred pounds, and that I was thinking about pursuing the career path of mathematics and data analysis, his hat was off to me. He uttered the words, "Fair play to you, you have it all figured out."

I smiled, covering up the fact that I was going through a deep depression, and that heartbreak-induced feelings, among other internal struggles, had ignited the long-dormant demons of being too small, bullied, laughed at, and disregarded. Like I said, there are some things that will never leave.

Most of us will never be ok, we'll just get better at dealing with it. I hope the flashbacks make sense now.

It became clear to me that, no matter how perfect the life of an individual appears to the outside world, and no matter how happy we think an individual should feel about their situation, it's their interpretation of their life that defines their happiness. Your perception is your reality.

The colour was draining from my face. I wasn't dying, but I looked like it. I've had many interesting conversations with people about death, and the afterlife. But the most interesting one, I had with a former work colleague. He put forward the proposal that we are forms of energy. Energy, by the laws of physics, cannot be created or destroyed. So, when we die, we can't just disappear. The energy has to go somewhere. The idea has genuinely kept me awake at night sometimes.

So, fair enough, we don't know what happens when we die. But what happens when we feel like we've died? What happens in our darkest hours?

We all go through hard times, and we never know what's going to push us over the edge. Often, it can be something that doesn't appear all that detrimental to the outside world. Again, your perception is your reality. As I stared at my reflection, forgetting to blink, my stomach turned again thinking back to my darkest days, supposedly having it all sorted, but feeling absolutely numb.

But that was just my experience. In conversations with people, I've heard of stories far worse than mine. Conflicts, internal and external, far more sinister than anything I can recall in my own life.

We may all go through a negative and unpleasant experience that leaves us questioning ourselves. There may come a time when we feel dead inside. We may feel that we have nothing left to give, or offer, of any value to ourselves or those around us.

But those moments mould us as people. When you've died inside once already, you don't really give a fuck anymore. The opinions of those that pass by hold much less weight, and you find an unquestionable value in the things that you hold dear to your heart. You're in your bonus minutes and anything can happen.

From then on, you feel compelled to live in a way that pleases you, for the simple reason that you know that the clock is ticking. It's like the end of a football match; you're in stoppage time, and you're aware that the whistle can blow at any minute. You become grateful for every extra second that you get.

I was breathing heavily still, unsure of whether my insides had settled or not. I ran the cold tap and threw water over my face in an attempt to calm down. As the droplets fell from my forehead down onto the ceramic surface, I paused. I watched how the water formed a circular pattern, away from the plughole, before flowing in. My mind drifted to movie scenes of casinos, roulette tables, and that sort of thing. A ball is thrown in, and follows a circular path, before falling on either red or black. In the same way, if I was to throw the ball into the sink in front of me, it would travel the same circular path as the water, before falling into the plughole.

Now, I would be lying if I said that I was suicidal during these darkest hours. I've had conversations with people who have been in that mind frame, and others who have tried, some on more than one occasion, to take their own lives. It's a unique mindset.

It is said that people take their own lives due to being in a dark place, with very little hope of things ever improving, and I can vouch for that, given what I have heard from those close to me.

Personally, I could relate to the sense of hopelessness, and the feeling that I was trapped in a horrible reality that might not change. So, imagine the sink in front of me again. Imagine the water flowing. Say I throw a roulette ball into the sink. It will follow this circular pattern before disappearing down the drain.

The basin of the sink is like a pit, or a hole, a place of hopelessness, and depression. Think of it as the point before being suicidal. The drain itself is the realm of being truly ready to take your own life. It's much easier to get out of the sink than it is to get out of the drain, but in both cases, the ball can be retrieved. So, in those delicate months in 2018, I found myself on this tidal wave of unhappiness and confusion, very close to this plughole.

My mind was running riot as I stared at my reflection. The thought of Avicii's death replaced the flashbacks in my head with music. Lyrics that had affected me were filtering through the back of my mind; I've always found that music stays with us. Reality welcomed me back from my lyrical daydream with another rush of blood, as I coughed up the remainder of my insides.

Was it Normal to be like this?

Was it Normal to go this far into your own head? Was this in the Handbook?

Did depression get an honourable mention?

Was there a template eulogy for the funerals of those who took their own lives due to an inability to live by the requirements of the Normal regime?

I took a deep breath, making every attempt to calm down.

Those darkest hours led me to a change of heart. The way that I viewed life changed in a sense. The best way I can explain it is by using music.

Everyone's taste in music is different. Finley, my previously mentioned continental friend, got me interested in acoustic covers, and in-studio performances. They were raw, I suppose, and a musician's talent shone through a lot more. One of my favourite songs is Ed Sheeran's 'Don't'. In a live in-studio performance on YouTube, Ed's ability with nothing but a guitar and a loop pedal is genius. He creates a loop of three or four guitar sequences, or strumming patterns, before beginning to sing.

So, it got me thinking.

Our conscience, our perception of right and wrong, our values, and our entire moral standpoint is like a loop, a constant underlying tune. This loop is formed based on different factors, like our upbringing, and our environment. Now, Ed usually sings the lyrics that we are familiar with in a live performance, and then sometimes breaks into a freestyle rap, throwing in lines that we haven't heard before. This is a form of expression. Ed hits us with different lyrics, but the loop remains unchanged. Ed's singing is an example of the things we do spontaneously, such as speak and think. Our words and thoughts may drastically change, but our moral standpoint remains relatively unaffected day to day.

However, every so often in life, something may happen that changes this loop; in essence, changing our values, our morals, and the nature of our conscience. This can be anything; relocating to a place with a different culture, or a different way of living, a bereavement, a break-up, a family conflict, a broken friendship, anything. In order to rebuild this loop, to form it appropriately based on our experiences and the several changes in our lives, the old loop must be broken.

The music stops. There is a brief silence.

In this silence, we may feel lost, and confused. But don't fear the silence. It's necessary. Confusion is a necessity for the founding of a new moral standpoint, and repertoire of values. In the silence, remember, the new loop being formed may be far superior to the previous one. The silence is where the growth takes place. So, the next time you tell someone to 'change their tune', remember that it isn't easy, and that yours may change when you're at your most vulnerable.

My mind flashed back to late-night drives, coming home from night shifts, being eaten alive by the quiet roads, and the thoughts in my head. During the darkest hours, I was being exposed to an emotion that I hadn't really encountered before; guilt. Love and fear are powerful, but guilt puts on a different show, manifesting itself through shaking hands and a turned stomach.

Before that point in 2018, I had never really wronged, or hurt anybody. I had no such thing as guilt anywhere on my conscience. The concept of ending a relationship on bad terms meant that I had bad blood with certain people. The likelihood of me ever seeing them again was slim, but the main problem was this; how could I look at myself and consider myself a good person, when there were people in this world who had a terrible opinion of me?

I had this false idea that to be a good-natured person, you had to be liked, or at least tolerated, by everybody. Now, I said before that I never cared about fitting in or being liked, and that was true. But being conscious of the fact that you are disliked is different. It weighs heavier on you.

I can clarify straight away that what I had in my head was a severe dose of people-pleasing; a very toxic trait that appears brilliant to others, but it can eventually take its toll on the individual.

You can't please everyone, and the faster you learn that, the happier you will be.

Guilt plays another role in our lives.

We're told that it's ok not to be ok. But more often than not, we don't feel like we have the right nor do we consider ourselves worthy to feel the way that we do. When we find ourselves in a bad headspace, we often compare ourselves to others, who we think are going through similar problems. We make ourselves feel guilty for feeling upset or anxious about a certain situation.

If you find yourself in a dark frame of mind, don't beat yourself up about it. Some things in life require a grieving process, or perhaps a short period of reflection. This is ok. We all have our problems.

But don't get too caught up looking in a broken wing mirror. The windscreen may be fogged up, but it will eventually clear.

As I stared down into the sink, I was reminded of how 'not ok' it can get. I was reminded of how it can seem as if all is lost, but I was grateful for what I had learned. I said before that there are three things in life you find without looking, in no particular order, I might add. The first one is your family. The second one is your purpose. Purpose is defined as the reason for which something is created, or for which something exists; in essence, our reason for being here.

My survival of the Monkey's regime and the fluke crash made sense now. Your purpose can be anything. It may manifest itself in many ways, but it will all boil down to one answer. The only problem is that you never know when you're going to find it. And sometimes, it may take a bad experience or two to bring it to the surface.

A sense of purpose can truly save us, or at least I can say that it saved me. Purpose was life's hand that reached into the sink and took me out of the water's flow.

I stood up straight and looked in the mirror again.

The gaunt ghost gasped for air, before disappearing into the past again, banished by the colour that was slowly returning to my face. My heart began to slow down, and with that, my balance finally made an appearance. Taking one last deep breath, in a futile attempt to process the last few minutes, I slowly left the bathroom.

As I cautiously descended the stairs, the beautiful blend of music and conversation wafted in through the downstairs hallway. The few steps that I took through the kitchen allowed me an interval of preparation as I ventured from the peace of the house to the energy of the outdoors.

I was met by an unchanged scene as I re-entered the garden. My eyes panned across the vicinity before arriving at the Stranger, who was scrolling through his phone, seemingly disconnected from all the chat around him.

I took my glass from the arm of the chair and refilled it. Sitting back down, I lifted the cigarette and held it in my right hand once again. There were no amateur dramatics on the Stranger's behalf; no big deal was made out of my momentary absence. He just put his phone down and carried on.

"You ok, my friend?"

I sighed heavily, now much more at ease. After a quick nod of clarification, I allowed myself a second to return to the present moment.

"I thought you were cracking up," he added.

I remained silent for another moment or two, before sitting forward.

"I may very well have been saved one night, a few weeks after coming home from college. Friends of mine had sat the leaving cert, and we were out for a few quiet drinks. I was in... probably the lowest depths of my darkest hours. My friends were conscious of this, and for a large portion of the early evening, as we sat in the beer garden, most eyes were on me. Questions were fired across. How was I? Were things improving? How did I feel?... I eventually snapped out of this self-indulgent daze that I was in, and turned to my friends to return the favour. Everyone has their problems, and I didn't want all the focus to be on me. So, I asked a few of them how they were. Don't ask me what was in the air, or the gin that night, but a few of my friends began to open up about one or two matters... I realised that I had a way of listening. Others felt comfortable to talk to me about their problems. One of the girls completely opened up. She spoke to me for hours, about a number of things. As the conversation progressed, I realised something further... I could relate any problem that was presented to me back to an experience in my own life. It dawned on me; bullying, low self-esteem, rejection, heartbreak, failure and family conflict were a few of my familiar areas. I had some way of relating every story that I heard back to one of those experiences. I was able to help someone with anecdotes of my own; stuff I genuinely felt inside. Life showed me in the space of a few hours, that I had more to give, and that I was needed. Life showed me my purpose."

He remained silent for a few moments, before removing the cigarette from his mouth.

"So, that's where all these 'conversations' started," he said. "Your purpose, your way of giving back".

I nodded in agreement, as I lifted the glass from the arm of the chair.

"Life had truly cracked me. But all for good reason. My maths teacher had a point about this whole 'June' thing. June 2017 showed me a new life. June 2018 gave me a reason to keep living."

14

The Fight

I remained silent for a few seconds, allowing myself to properly return to the present. Everything seemed a bit quieter than it had been before my trip to the bathroom, or maybe that was just my perception. In my head, it felt like those few seconds after disaster strikes in a film, after a tsunami or a bomb or something like that; a peculiar blend of silence and chaos.

The Stranger sat back with folded arms, again exercising immaculate patience. "You had a rough few weeks," he said hoarsely, before clearing his throat.

I nodded, before looking down into my glass. It was about time that he got closure as to how I became a more 'seasoned drinker'.

Despite the sense of purpose stepping in and 'saving me', I was still in a deep depression. It felt different to the first time that I had properly battled with it, at the mercy of the Monkey. I was much more self-aware this time. My self-esteem was shattered, and to be honest, I felt pathetic. The feeling of being comfortable in my own skin had properly faded away.

For me, the fight against depression was based on what I would later call 'momentum through achievement'. I realized that, when everything is going well, it's easy to stay disciplined and to work hard. For example, if you have just got a job promotion, then driving through rush-hour traffic is going to feel a lot easier. If you're in the gym and seeing consistent results, then it's easier to keep training and eating right. If you're scoring every time you step on a football field, then it's easier to keep giving it your all.

But when things go wrong, it's much harder to stay focused. When you get injured, or when you don't get the pay-rise that you were expecting, things become more difficult. Your momentum is broken, and you can become discouraged by your setbacks.

That's how depression feels; all momentum is gone. I had lost the spring in my step, and my overall energy. Getting through the day was a task and going to work to deal with the public was particularly difficult.

So, I started to make small changes.

This may sound clichéd, but if you find yourself struggling to fight depression, start by making your bed. Start by tidying the house; keep a clean kitchen, and a tidy bedroom. I've found that those small changes can help you regain a bit of the momentum that depression takes away.

Given that my self-esteem was shot to pieces, how I carried and presented myself was my first area of focus. I started dressing differently, going from wearing t-shirts and jerseys to polo shirts. I found that when I dressed well, I felt good in myself. Working in a bar helped this. Next thing you know, I was wearing brown suit shoes and long-sleeved shirts every day of the week.

Self-improvement and a feeling of personal progress were my main ammunition in this fight to regain my momentum. This was the long-term side of the battle. As effective as this method was, it didn't always satisfy in the short term. The weekly fight against depression had another, much less recommended, but much more common methodology.

My friends were all home from college for the summer, and everyone seemed to be missing the buzz of going out three nights a week. So, to combat the boredom of rural living and full-time work, we would all congregate for a communal session of a weekend. I hadn't really found the taste nor the tolerance for drinking yet, so by the time two or three vodkas were onboard, I would start to get tipsy.

And then, over a few weeks, the appeal started to dawn on me. For a few hours, I would stop thinking. I started to understand Micky Flanagan's idea of 'The Dreaded Flavour'. It didn't really matter to me where we were, whether it be in a nightclub or a quiet bar; alcohol still had the same effect.

Now, of course, being in good company is also a huge help. Time with those you care about is a priceless commodity, especially when you're struggling mentally. But alcohol had a way of getting me out of my own head and putting me at ease.

It can do a lot of other things too, I won't lie. It can put you back into your own head just as quick. It can lead you to incredibly bad decisions; I'm sure we can all relate. I've drunk and driven once in my time, and I'm lucky to be alive *after it. But what really stood out to me were the conversations that alcohol led me to, conversations that I will never forget till the day I die.*

People will talk about anything when they have a few drinks in them. Absolutely anything.

The Stranger looked at the bottle of vodka that I was slowly murdering, and then back at me.

"A brief escape from your own head."

"It's not the amount I drank that was worrying," I replied. "It was the manner in which I turned to it. If you met me in May, and then again in August, my tolerance had grown tenfold. But you're right, it was an escape."

"I understand. Tell me about these drunk conversations you ended up having."

I smiled, filtering through the mound of nonsense verbal memorabilia in my head.

This is probably going to sound a bit juvenile but bear with me. The first real 'drunk conversation' that I ever had, took place while walking back to a friend's house; roughly eleven miles we calculated, using drunk intuition. Adam was, and still is, one of the wittiest men I've ever come across.

As we walked, slowly sobering up, we began to talk about music, and Adam asked me if I had ever heard the song, 'No Vaseline'. I had never really listened to rap music other than the mainstream content of Eminem, so in terms of rap history, I hadn't even broken the surface. As I listened to Ice Cube almost end the careers of four of his life-long friends, I was introduced to a whole new culture.

In the weeks after this early morning stroll, I began to indulge in the likes of Ice Cube, NWA, and Eminem. There were a few take-home points that I found; rap music, for me, was proof of the power of relatability. Eminem's songs, in particular, showed me that inspiration can most definitely come from a very dark place. When you yourself are in a dark frame of mind, it's those lyrics, and those expressions of raw emotion that really speak to you. Honest recollections of hardships and struggles, although they don't appeal to everyone, can really strike a chord, no pun intended, with those who need to hear them. We're reminded that we're not alone in our struggles, in a sense, and that pain is a universal concept.

On the other end of the genre, NWA's music shone a light on the idea of authenticity. Their music pretty much started a social revolution; in essence, the expression of truth can have a profound effect.

Truth, and relatability. I realised very quickly that it was those two elements that defined the conversation that had saved me in June. It was my honesty about my problems that really helped someone else, so I slowly came to terms with my experiences, and became less 'embarrassed', or 'afraid of judgement' for my mental struggles. I thought to myself, 'I'm proud of the life that I've lived'.

I became a bit more positive about things. Everything happens for a reason, and those reasons were slowly beginning to show themselves. I began to hold my head up a bit higher. You can argue that I'm taking moral wisdom from the wrong sources, but if life has taught me anything, it's that you will find inspiration in the strangest of places.

The Stranger paused for a second.

"You were putting the pieces together, but Jesus Christ, you were pulling them out of random places."

"True enough," I replied. I sat back and surveyed the scene again for a brief moment, before returning my eyes to the ground.

"Regardless of the pieces themselves, the gym was the glue that was going to hold them together. Powerlifting is the one thing I have to credit for helping me cope, more than anything. As always, it was the key ingredient in my self-improvement, and without it, I would have probably drunk a lot more. Training was a release of negative energy, and pent-up emotions, I suppose. You said when you sat down that people become like wild animals before they go out and lift. I never really understood it before. But that summer, it sank in. Energy that's spurred on by negative emotions is... is a different branch of performance. Physical ability is... enhanced... by training, recovery and nutrition, they say. But the adrenaline that comes from being in the darkest depths of your own head can really help. It's not a pleasant place to be, but if you find yourself there, you can make good use of it."

I paused and turned my focus back to the Stranger.

"I had planned to compete again on November 17th. It was two days before I turned twenty, so I wanted my last performance as a teenager to be a memorable one. I made a promise that I'd deadlift a quarter of a tonne, or 250 kilos. There was no reason. I just picked a number that would test me."

The Stranger removed the cigarette from his mouth. "Was that a reasonable jump from the lift in May?"

"Not exactly," I replied, as I thought back to when I first had the idea. "When I arrived back in Galway and told my teammates, there were a few rolling eyes. But I don't blame them."

"Perhaps they were just being realistic and keeping your feet on the ground." I took a drink and rested the glass on my leg.

"I once read this; If you have an idea that's accepted by everybody the first time that they hear it, then the idea is not big enough. Remember that the next time someone talks down your thought process. I had nothing to lose. Like I said earlier, this wasn't external pressure, this was an internal desire. This was fulfilment. And November 17th was definitely going to be a moment that money couldn't buy."

The Stranger cleared his throat as he sat forward slightly.

"You were a different man when you arrived back in Galway, I'd imagine, given the summer that you had."

I nodded in agreement and prepared myself for the unloading of a few months that changed my life.

15

Family

By the time I arrived back in Galway in September, I was a different person. I still had my demons, but I was a lot more confident, and a lot more comfortable in my own skin. The summer had served me well in that sense, and on top of that, my drinking tolerance was admirable, to say the least.

The first new man I met in second year was Ciaran. On the first night back, he hosted a house party to help his cousin's friend meet a few new people. Needless to say, with thirty of us there, and a noise complaint for good measure, we made him feel welcome. I arrived late and played catch-up, drinking half a litre of vodka in about fifteen minutes. To put it simply, Ciaran's first impression of me was a memorable one.

Throughout the remainder of the first week, Ciaran and I became close friends. It seemed timeless, as if he had been there all along. Time means nothing when it comes to friendship. Sometimes, you can just click with people instantly. Between Ciaran's presence and my size, neither of us went unnoticed in a room full of people. I was well able to talk, but Ciaran was different. He had the room in his hands; a chandelier that wasn't bound to the ceiling. Like me, he has an accent that stands out in Galway like a sore thumb. Everything seemed that bit funnier when he or I said it. It's like we said earlier, natural entertainers.

In the days that followed, Ciaran and I began to talk less about irrelevant nonsense, and more about life. We would all gather in some random apartment for pre-drinks, and he and I would often end up standing chatting in a hallway, or outside while he smoked, talking about everything and anything. I can't remember whether it was he or I who opened up first, but once one of us began talking, the other followed.

Ciaran told me that he had very little self-confidence, and he talked to me about how the pressure of the leaving cert drove him into a deep depression. But what really got me about Ciaran, was the fact that he wasn't at all content with how he felt in his own skin.

"Wait, wait, wait, hang on. Him?" the Stranger asked in disbelief, as he pointed at Ciaran.

I nodded silently.

We both looked over at him, a bottle in his hand, deep in conversation with a few other good characters.

"Him," I said quietly. "The most confident man in the room." In shock, the Stranger turned his attention back in my direction.

"As I opened up to Ciaran about my own life, he found some relatability in my experiences. I spoke about my own feelings of depression... how getting bigger saved me from being bullied, and how powerlifting helped me to find a sense of identity. I told him everything, really. But the main message Ciaran took, from me and from others, is that you can be who you want to be as a person... You

127

can recreate yourself, regardless of your past. Ciaran showed me that everyone has layers to them. He was one of the 'natural entertainers', with a few demons living rent-free in his head. Throughout the week, I met some of his extended group of friends. They were just like him; a joy to be around, and a presence in the room... But at half-past three in the morning, when everyone had arrived back from the night's grasp, they were the same people who would talk to me about everything and anything. People that I had only met hours before were spilling out tales of their own mental struggles, as well as listening to whatever problems and advice that I presented to them in return."

I paused and sighed heavily as I recalled those conversations.

"You really never know what's going on behind the closed doors of the lives of the people you meet," I said. "Everyone is fighting an internal battle."

The Stranger was in shock. He kept looking over at Ciaran, and then back at me. "The funny thing is, if you had met him ten months ago when I did, he wouldn't have seemed any different. The only people that really notice the difference are those close to him. It's the undercover conversations, behind closed doors and windows, that really tell you how a person is feeling inside."

The Stranger eventually believed me. "I take it that he's family then."

I smiled, looking over in Ciaran's direction.

"You can bet on that. And he's not the only family member I found at the time. Life knew that I was in a bad place and gave me what I needed to pull through."

Ciaran's house party that got a noise complaint on night one was hosted to help his cousin's friend, Tiernan. Tiernan was a bit quieter than Ciaran, and a bit more reserved. But like Ciaran, he had his layers.

He and I had a lengthy conversation on the second night. Again, I only knew him for about twenty-four hours, but I found myself standing in the hallway of an apartment talking to him. He spoke about his family, and how tight-knit they were. He opened up about bereavement and told me that he was alone with his grandfather, essentially his best friend, when he passed away. I broke down, unable to hold back the tears.

Tiernan showed a calmness when he spoke. He showed acceptance in everything that he said, and an open-mindedness towards everything that I said. But our main similarity was that we were both old before our time. His maturity was something to behold.

What I admired most about Tiernan was his attitude. He was an extremely driven commerce student, and one of the first things he ever said to me was, "I'll be a millionaire at thirty". He wasn't afraid to aim high, a trait of his which helped me in ways that I can't even put into words. I raised my glass to him, and with slurred words, I informed both he and Ciaran that I was going to lift a quarter of a tonne. They were open-minded fellas and patted me on the back.

During Ciaran's recollections of his depression, he mentioned two names; two girls who were by his side through thick and thin; Avril and Olivia. I met both of them

129

shortly after meeting Ciaran. They're, to quote Ciaran directly, 'the same, but different'. They're two incredible people. I won't lie, Avril scared the life out of me at first. She has a way of seeing through everyone's bullshit, and she can tell within five minutes if you're genuine or not. She's the mother of the group, in a sense, there for everyone when they need her. She's like Ciaran; the life of the room. Olivia's more like Tiernan. She's more reserved and quieter, but only slightly; the cool aunt of the group. It only took a matter of days for me to realise that I was in good hands. I had found friends that I could safely call family.

"Character always appears at the right time," the Stranger said with a smile. "It's mad what happens in seven days. They say freshers' week is an experience, but I wasn't expecting that... I found a huge sense of belonging. Those conversations about life and personal struggles concreted my sense of purpose and took my mind off my own problems. I promised myself that if anyone on a night out expressed any desire to talk, then I would be there to listen; in a smoking area, or in one of the apartments beforehand, it didn't matter. I would be there for whoever needed help."

The Stranger smiled.

This was his area of expertise.

"You never know when people are going to start talking," he said. "In the same sense, I bet you didn't see this coming when you arrived here a few hours ago. The day can just take a turn."

I laughed quietly. I *hadn't* seen this conversation coming. But I was very much relieved that it did.

"Talking changes everything. And that's not just the case with problems and negative emotions. I've found that talking about your goals can be a massive help. Saying them out loud puts the idea into your own head and the heads of those around you. I told everyone close to me that I intended to lift a quarter of a tonne. Next thing you know, eight or ten people had November 17th marked as a red-letter day."

I rotated the glass on the arm of the chair, before taking another drink. The Stranger remained silent for a moment or two.

"What really strikes me... What strikes me is how much mutual respect there was between you and these new people. I mean, you had only just met them, and yet you were there for one another."

I smiled, as my eyes wandered around the scene in front of me.

"The second pillar of good character; open-mindedness. These new people around me displayed it in bucket-loads. What comes with open-mindedness is a respect for the opinions... and ambitions... of those around you, even if you don't fully agree with them. It's a sense of accepting that not everyone is going to think, and act, like you do. It's a mindful state that I encountered very little of when I was growing up, given that it completely undermines the sacred Handbook. But nevertheless, I found it in this group of people."

"You had always craved respect. And now you had an abundance of it." I couldn't help but smile.

"Indeed," I replied. "For the first time ever, respect started coming from all angles. And I've a good story about that."

16

Respect and Attention

I found myself in a dense queue at a bar one night, a few weeks into the semester. Working thirty hours every weekend meant that I felt like I had money to burn, so I was going through a weird phase of tipping every bartender that I came across.

I stumbled across the floor to the table adjacent to the bar, with Jägerbombs in-hand. Every stool was taken, so I stood to one side, on the outskirts of the bubbling conversation. As I quietly surveyed the scene, one guy from the passing crowd of people stopped to talk to me. I had no clue who he was, but he approached me politely.

"Man, you're in serious shape," he said, holding his right hand out to shake mine. I was wearing a short-sleeved shirt, and by this point, I wasn't far off thirteen stone. Recognition from strangers, and steroid accusations from ill-informed customers in the bar at home, had both become a regular occurrence.

I thanked him for his kind words, and he leaned in to speak to me again, shouting over the music.

"I'm trying to lose weight, and I was wondering if you had any advice?" he asked me, or at least words to that effect. I ushered him out towards the smoking area to have a proper conversation. This gentleman informed me

that he had already lost about three kilos, but he was hoping to lose another ten or so. I advised him to keep doing what he was doing, given that he was seeing progress, but I also let him in on my own daily intake of food, or at least the bits of it that I could recall in my inebriated state.

We discussed exercise, and I encouraged him to speak to a coach, or someone experienced, before venturing into a gym. I stressed the importance of proper technique when it came to lifting weights, and how that importance can slip from your mind as a beginner.

Once all those matters had been discussed, I asked him how he felt in himself since his transformation had begun. His reply was exactly what I had expected. "I feel far better in myself already, it's just really hard to keep going," he said, shrugging his shoulders slightly. I understood his pain. So, I shuffled the deck of my memories to help this kind gentleman.

"Here's how you can look at it," I said, and once again I must emphasise, words to that effect. "Imagine one day when you've lost the weight that you want to lose. Imagine how much better you will feel in yourself. Your body will feel the benefit; your heart, your lungs, everything. Picture that day in your head and keep it there."

I stopped to finish the rest of my concoction of Jäger, and what felt like a hybrid of Red Bull and petrol, before continuing.

"Then when that day comes, focus on maintaining that newfound health, and not slipping back into old habits. I *know it may seem a long way off, and right now you may feel like you'll never get there. But look me up and down. A few years ago, I was on the verge of starving because of anorexia. But I believed that I could change."*

He looked me up and down two or three times in the following moments. I dropped my plastic glass, not for dramatic effect or anything, but because I was getting very invested in the conversation and needed my hands to make my point with appropriate emphasis. "And you can too," I said. "Just believe in it, my friend."

He appeared to be quite shaken by our conversation, and I really wouldn't blame him. After shaking my hand again, he called me an inspiration, thanked me, and went on his way. I bounced back to our table, on an absolute high, still not fully sure of what had just happened. But I proved my little rap music idea to myself; truth and relatability really have their ways of moving people.

The Stranger was baffled.

"He just came up to you out of the blue?"

"He did, and I admire him for it. It takes courage to approach a complete stranger in that manner, and I hope our conversation served him well. Hopefully, I was the character that he needed to help push him a bit further."

"For all we know, you might have been the first person to show any belief in him. One thing is for certain though; he had the height of respect for you."

I paused for a second and took a deep breath.

"Respect is an incredible thing," I replied. "I once read that the difference between respect and attention is that respect lasts longer."

The Stranger laughed, as he brought his cigarette towards his mouth.

"It depends on who you're talking to, I suppose. Some people value attention far more."

He was right.

"Some people haven't a clue about the… renewable nature of respect, and the… the spontaneous combustion of attention. It's one of our generation's major flaws."

"And I suppose this flaw gave you an idea."

Let me create a scenario. There are five people watching a game, sitting around a tv. It could be soccer, rugby, or hurling for argument's sake. Let's suppose that two of the five people are engrossed in the game. We'll call these people A and B. The other three, C, D and E, have little to no interest, so they chat among themselves about literally anything other than what's on the screen.

A and B react to different occurrences in the game, like near misses, good tackles, and excellent passes. C, D and E notice these reactions but remain uninterested. Then, suppose a player gets injured; a striker gets elbowed in the face during a corner-kick, a full-back gets a hurl smashed across his helmet, or someone gets a knee into the jaw during a scrum. A and B are in audible shock, and insist that C, D and E take notice of what's happening, out of genuine human concern. Like I said, pain is a universal feeling, so the sight of blood dripping down a player's face is going to trigger you whether you like sports or not.

Let's say that after a couple of minutes of treatment, the injured player agrees to play on, despite his black eye, or his broken teeth. As he gets up to return to his position, all five people applaud his gallant effort. He is portraying courage and dedication, and all five people respect his actions. When the game restarts, C, D and E return to their conversation.

Remember when you were in school, and when a teacher caught you talking, you were told to 'pay attention'. There's a reason for that. Our attention is like a currency. When we pay our attention to a movie or a series on Netflix, in return, we want to be entertained. When we pay attention in school or college, we wish to be educated. You sit and pay attention to me, and in return, you want to be informed. Our attention is a finite entity, a currency that we use to pay for something in return.

Respect is different; it's renewable. You see, when we respect someone for their efforts or actions, we are uplifted by what they have done. We don't need anything in return, as the action that warrants respect is rewarding to both the provider and the witness. We 'pay attention', but we 'show some respect'.

The showing of respect can have many motives, or triggers, such as bravery, courage, morality and selflessness. These all have a common foundation, and that is the character of the individual portraying them. This is why respect is the basis of any good relationship or friendship. When we get to know the people that we meet, the respect that we show them is a testament to their character.

Attention is a bit different.

137

If we consider the receiving of respect to be a well-balanced breakfast, consisting of a bowl of porridge perhaps, and maybe a banana, then in comparison, attention is like a breakfast roll. It's far quicker to obtain, far nicer in the moment, particularly if you're hungover, but it's a bit more expensive, and you can't really live off it in the long run.

I'm waffling a bit, pardon the pun.

The Stranger laughed. "You really are full of shi-"
"Hang on, hang on. I'm getting there, I promise."

The receiving of attention's non-refundable payment is often generated by one very fragile motive, which is image. Now, I would be lying if I said that I don't love social media. Being honest, most of my news on global current affairs comes from memes. I would most certainly be lying if I said that I don't enjoy the comments of congratulations on posts I put up about gym personal bests, and lifts that I have done in competition. But what I've noticed, over time, is our generation's chronic reliance on external validation. We're all guilty of it to an extent. Instagram is probably the greatest source of this. The number of people I can think of that would have been deeply saddened by Instagram taking away the visual number of likes, is quite alarming.

For some people, their image and how they portray it is the fast track to an endorphin rush. To put it bluntly, I.M.A.G.E is the 'Intense Magnification of Absolutely Gross Egotism.' Let's pause for a second, and take out the letters M and E, 'Magnification', and 'Egotism'. If our feelings of self-worth and validation fluctuate majorly based on the number of likes we get, or the opinions of others in general, then the idea of what makes us the people that we are, is very much summed up in the letters M and E. Our behaviour ends up being a magnification of our own egotism.

I made a connection over time between external validation and the people that we meet. We all know that a lot of people in our lives come and go. As you leave school, and go to college and beyond, you learn this fairly quick.

Imagine this. You're standing on a factory floor. In front of you, there is a conveyor belt, moving from left to right. On this conveyor belt, are the people you meet as you go through life.

There are some people who will hop off the conveyor belt and stand by your side. Those people are what I call family. They will get off the belt of their own accord, just as life intended. They don't need to be called, ushered or prompted. It will happen like clockwork.

Then there are the people that you want to keep in your life that aren't meant to be there. These can be people who are a bad influence; those that don't bring out your best side. Or these can be the people that life sent to you for character development and growth; people that hurt you. Life hasn't given them the stamp of family, so they must keep going; they can't come off the belt. You may find it hard to let these people go, but remember that *if you try and hold onto them, you will get pulled off to the right, away from the family that life has intended for you.*

Then, of course, there are the people that you never really clicked with or got to know. They continue off to the right also, without you really caring.

This system works well, but there's one small problem.

To the far right of the conveyor belt, there's a door to let the unsuited people go. But for a lot of us, that door is locked by our reliance on external validation. Our need for approval from others makes it hard for us to let people out of our lives. As new people come in from the left, the conveyor belt becomes crowded, making it harder for the right people to find their way off to stand by your side.

Finding contentment in ourselves, without the need for the constant approval of others, really can make our lives much simpler, allowing us to see clearly the people that are meant to stay with us; the people who are family.

"Ok, fair enough, you got there in the end. I'll allow it," he said, laughing. I was really starting to admire the man sitting beside me. I had been talking all evening, barely letting him get a line in, yet he hung off my every word. I was grateful for his presence, but even more so for his character.

"What made you think of all that?" he asked.

I watched the cigarette in my hand as I rolled it between my fingers.

"Like you said, I've had the pleasure of knowing people who put attention on a very high pedestal. I got to witness all this first-hand. None of this is hearsay," I replied.

I rested my head back and gathered my thoughts, as I felt the vodka go to my head slightly.

"I learned something over time about social media, now that I think of it. Between slowly finding myself and my family, I really stopped caring about the opinions of outsiders, and people from my past. So, I opened Instagram one day, and unfollowed about three hundred people. I was fed up of seeing life updates about folks I hadn't spoken to in a couple of years. I started to follow accounts about entrepreneurship, motivation, and things like that. Within a few weeks, my newsfeed had completely changed. I realised that your newsfeed is very much a reflection of your thought process. If you're continuously scrolling through the daily adventures of other people, your focus is going to drift away from your own life, and you will end up getting caught in the hamster wheel."

The Stranger lifted his head from his hand. "What do you mean by the hamster wheel?" he asked.

The poor fella, I was hitting him with several ideas at once.

"Comparison," I answered. "It's like a hamster wheel; it'll keep you busy, but it'll get you nowhere. Comparing yourself to other people, to their lives and their achievements, is equivalent to running inside this metal confinement. If you keep doing it for long enough, then you're going to be exhausted, and mentally drained. When you stop, you'll be in the exact same place as you were when you started. You will have made no progress, and now you have no energy to focus on yourself."

He remained silent for a moment.

"I suppose we're all guilty of that from time to time."

"Believe me," I replied. "I've learned from comparing myself to friends, sporting opponents, teammates; basically everyone. You'll never be happy if you keep comparing. Focus on you, and don't mind anyone else."

I got up and made my way towards the bottle of vodka, which was very much on its last legs. After refilling the glass, I made a conscious attempt to walk in a straight line back to the chair. As I sat down, my neck muscles felt weak and I struggled to keep my head straight. My eyelids felt heavy, and I could feel a numbing sensation move down through my jaw. Drunk Conor and Sober Conor were performing a two-man play, but as the final act began, neither character was sure of their lines.

17

Brotherhood

My empty stare across the patio was interrupted by the Stranger's cloud of exhaled smoke. I never really understood the concept of smoking. You force yourself to enjoy the inhalation of toxic chemicals, and then you can't quit. But then again, it's an addiction. It's on the same page as alcohol and drugs in a sense. It's something we do for enjoyment. When I look at it in that sense, my questioning grinds to a halt. My mother's youngest sibling, David, is only six years my senior, so growing up he was more like a brother than an uncle. He used to always tell me; "Conor, we're here for a good time, not for a long time." He's not wrong. I've always been one to look after the future now, but at the same time, I would rather die young doing what I love than to live till eighty living a life that never satisfied me.

As the Stranger removed the ash from his cigarette, I interrupted the deafening silence.

"Have you ever seen the film "Rush"?"

"I have," he replied. "I love Formula One."

My eyes met the ground again.

"Throughout the whole movie, Niki Lauda is portrayed as this intelligent, methodical character," I said. "He's a very sensible man with his head screwed on. Then, in contrast, you have James Hunt, an absolute lunatic."

The Stranger nodded in agreement.

"I suppose. But sometimes lunacy works in our favour; in the end, it's James Hunt who wins the World Championship."

"He took risks beyond belief. He put his life on the line. That dangerous sense of freedom when you have absolutely nothing to lose...it consumes you."

The Stranger sat forward slightly. "Have you ever felt that way?"

I sighed heavily and rested my head back, as I focused my eyes on the wall across from me.

"I felt that way for about ten minutes. It came, and it went. But I'll tell you one thing; I'll take those precious seconds to the grave with me."

As I took a drink, the insides of my mouth felt numb and my sense of taste began to disappear. It was time to raise a glass to the people I call family.

As the September session ground to a halt, I had about seven or eight weeks before November 17th. I put myself on a drinking ban. If I really wanted the quarter tonne to come off the ground, then I had to be on top form. The fear of failure was starting to set in slowly. Everyone close to me knew about the idea, and I couldn't let them down.

Stepping away from my short-term armour against depression led me to a difficult few weeks. Like I said before, the dust settled, and everything went quiet. The severity of my failed relationship started to really sink in, as I stepped away from the nights out.

The aftermath of a break-up is a confusing time. You suddenly realise the hollow nature of emotionless sex and the empty egotism that stems from hopping from one girl to another. Your emotions of affection form a short circuit and temporarily burn your ability to be kind and caring. You can become quite cold, and simply, quite numb. It's an experience, to say the least.

Feelings of inadequacy swamped my emotional radar. So, I did what I always do. I took these emotions and put them on a bar in front of me. It felt like every kilogram represented one negative thought.

You find your purpose and your family. The third entity in life, which you find without looking, is your escape. Your escape is your method of getting away from everything and everyone. This can be anything, like playing music, reading, going for a drive, literally anything at all. Whatever makes you feel most at ease, that's your escape. Many of us use alcohol and a good time to take our minds away from life's stresses, and there's nothing wrong with that. But a reliance on this can be dangerous. Our escape is a healthy and mindful method of stepping away from everyday life. Ciaran's escape is music, for example. I found mine in the form of metal bars and plates. Even when I trained with a team around me, I was alone as I approached the bar.

It was just me, the weight, and my emotions.

During these few weeks, Ciaran and Tiernan were there for me day and night. We had countless conversations venturing into the little hours of the morning. A lot of the time, Tiernan would listen as either me or Ciaran spoke. Ciaran and I had the common ground of depression, and the desire to be respected and valued. I was the designated driver of the group, and the three of us spent many late nights in Salthill, sitting on the stone wall looking out at the water.

They say that men don't talk. Give them the right company and the sense of security and see what happens. They'll pour out everything.

Ciaran's self-confidence took a hit when a short relationship fell apart. As a family, we made sure that he got through it. I've learned that nothing brings people together like hardship. In a conversation with Ciaran, I may have jinxed something by saying the words, "As bad as this situation is, if Tiernan's relationship ended, he would have to be on suicide watch". A couple of days later I received a text. Tiernan's girlfriend of nearly three years had left. In less than a few weeks, she became involved with a college friend, a friend that had been on the scene weeks before she had left Tiernan. The finger of logic pointed at possible infidelity. Regardless of the truth, that's the idea that formed in Tiernan's head. Much like my own situation, the demons of inadequacy began playing five-a-side in his mind. I now had even more common ground with him. I knew that he was in the sink.

The Stranger exhaled heavily.

"Jesus Christ," he said. "It's like they say, everything that can go wrong, will go wrong."

I didn't flinch, blink or even breathe.

"This lift was getting a build-up, to say the least," I replied.

I returned my stare to the ground and dived back into my memories.

When November 17th rolled around, the lift was no longer just something personal. The training that had manifested itself as a form of self-improvement, had now become a symbol. Family was the character that appeared for me at the right time; now it was my turn to return the favour. If I could pull this, then, as a unit. we could get through anything in a sense.

A powerlifting competition is a long, spread out event. Caffeine and adrenaline fill the air, along with rivalry, passion, and a bit of AC/DC. Squatting 220 kilos, and bench-pressing 150 at only nineteen years old led to handshakes and congratulations. People were patting me on the back and praising me; teammates, opponents and spectators. My appreciation was boundless, but I had only one thing on my mind.

For every lift, an athlete has three attempts. After my second deadlift of 230 kilos, I took a seat beside my teammates. I had ten minutes. My phone was broken, so listening to music was out of the question. I sat, hunched forward, with an empty can of Monster in my hands.

The caffeine was hitting me hard, gifting me with shaking hands. My right leg trembled as I bowed my head, and let my thoughts run riot. I bottled up everything. I thought of every football game when I sat unused on the side-line. I thought of every harsh comment, every laugh, every time that I felt like less than someone else. Every feeling of condescension, inadequacy, and failure were lined up against a wall in my mind. As I twisted the can, breaking the metal bit by bit, my adrenaline spiked.

A teammate took the can away from me, out of fear that I would cut my skin. Without looking up, I released my grasp on the yellow aluminium, and placed my hands at the top of my forehead, squeezing my skull.

My opponents took their third attempts one by one, with each lift heavier than the previous. As the clock wore down, I stood up, making my way to the chalk bowl. I heard my name, followed by the weight on the bar. As my coach gave his words of inspiration, and a slap on the back, I stepped forward.

Ciaran and Tiernan's pain took a seat in the crematorium of my thoughts. In less than a few seconds, I had a conversation with myself.

I would rather have been escorted out of that gym in a wheelchair than to let my family down.

I didn't want to see a life where I had failed them, and myself.

This was a message to the people I held dearest, and a middle finger to my past.

I was knee-deep in the dangerous freedom of having nothing to lose.

As I stood up with a quarter of a tonne in my hands, my vision returned to the room around me. The referee's hand dropped, and as I lowered the weight to the floor, I returned to reality.

The Stranger rested his bottle on the arm of the chair. "It's far more than just a sport to you, isn't it?"

"Definitely," I replied, as my voice went quiet. "It moulded me into who I am." Taking a long drag on his cigarette, the Stranger sat forward slightly.

"You mentioned purpose earlier. Did you ever feel like powerlifting was it? That strength was your reason for being here?"

I laughed quietly.

"For a long time, I did. At seventeen, I genuinely thought that one day I could be on World's Strongest Man. Like I said, I never aimed low. I've often joked that I'll be found dead one day, on the end of a bar weighing about four hundred kilos."

"Jesus. What a way to go." My eyes met the ground again.

"Life had shown me a sneak peek of my purpose through my drunken conversations, and this sense of purpose was only going to get stronger."

The beer ban came to an end, and I celebrated hard, in the sense that the night of my twentieth birthday, I didn't exactly come home, but rather I was found. Evidently, your tolerance goes to nothing when you don't drink for eight weeks.

As people congratulated me about the lift, I explained the priceless ten minutes to the close family. I walked them through the feelings; the out of body nature of it all. My recollection encouraged a few of my dearest friends to open up; those who hadn't already, of course. The number of people who had confessed mental struggles to me was now well into double figures. As always, I listened endlessly, and as usual, it took a few rounds of Jäger-bombs or double vodkas to get the talk flowing, pardon the pun.

What strikes me, and what will strike me till the day I die, is the severity of the matters that people keep to themselves. People would confess something to me; something that had a massive effect on themselves, or their families. Something that was taking a toll on them. They would then follow up with, "You're the first person I've ever said that to", or, "Jesus, I haven't talked about this in years."

It hit me.

The world that we live in.

We're so indoctrinated, so tied to the belief that talking, especially for men, is a sign of weakness. By the order of a blatant stigma, we would rather take our troubles to the grave, as they eat us alive, rather than talk about them. It made me physically sick to think that, in most cases I had witnessed, it took copious amounts of alcohol to get people to talk. People seemed afraid to speak. I always said that fear has its power, but this was another level.

The biscuit was well and truly taken one night in December when a dear friend of mine, who never really spoke about his emotions, completely opened up. He left me speechless with the words that he said. I could heavily relate to his problems, and the fact that he had never really spoken about them to anyone left me close to tears.

As I stood in Carbon Nightclub, with a double vodka in my hand, almost too drunk to speak, I had an idea. I wanted to have this recurring smoking area/nightclub conversation with a million people, but that wasn't physically possible. So, I downed my drink, and with slurred speech, I came out with the most ambitious idea that has ever crossed my mind.

I paused to take a drink.

The Stranger was heavily invested in my words and didn't appreciate my liquid interval.

"Which was…?" he asked.

I rested the glass on the arm of the chair, as I started to feel equally as drunk as I had that night, seven months before.

"I turned to my friend and I said, 'I'm going to write a book'."

The Stranger, for the first time that evening, portrayed a genuine expression of doubt.

"A book…" "Indeed."

He was silent for a few seconds, as another piece of the jigsaw fell into place. "Was this goal number three?"

"Yeah."

"But like… how?"

I pointed the cigarette at him to try and focus myself.

"I hadn't a clue," I exclaimed, as I looked him dead in the eye. "But I was going to try, because I would rather put everything on paper in the hope that it helps one person, than to live in a world where we can't talk. That's not an existence; that's a prison sentence."

The Stranger shook his head. "Fair enough, I suppose."

"However, before I could start writing, I had a couple more things to learn."

Drunk Conor was slowly starting to show himself. This was all his idea, so it was only right to let him talk.

18

Wisdom

As I took a drink, the Stranger and I scanned the surroundings. A few people had left, and those who remained were all indulged in their own conversations. Empty bottles were placed at random checkpoints around the patio, and a few cigarette butts hadn't quite reached the ashtrays, scattered beneath our feet like severed limbs in no man's land.

As I sat in the brief silence, I could feel the vodka going to my head, so before I spoke, I took a few seconds to avoid Drunk Conor's stutter.

"I had this module in college called Electromagnetism. It's literally just one theory to the next, and it makes very little sense if I'm honest. But the lecturer was brilliant. He caught me off guard one day; I was scrolling through Facebook when I heard him say the words, 'These laws weren't guessed; no-one just came up with them, they have a long and tortured history'. It was very philosophical for a maths lecture, in fairness, but I've thought about it a lot since. Then, I realised the acquisition of wisdom comes from 'a history'. Maybe the word 'tortured' is a bit strong, but wisdom requires experience; you can't just learn it, and you certainly can't teach it."

The Stranger laughed, as he shook his head.

"You're really scraping the bottom of the barrel for inspiration now." "Perhaps. But Keith was dead right. Knowledge and wisdom are two very different entities."

Remember what I said about school; how we're led to believe that a degree is the be-all and end-all of our chances in life. I'm not trying to put education down at all; it's incredibly powerful. But two of the wisest, and most intelligent people I have ever met, never went to college.

One of them is Kyle.

I learned from my father that people can be extremely intelligent, and particularly mechanically minded, without excelling on paper. Kyle is just that. When we left school, Kyle didn't go to third level. It didn't matter to him, however. He had ambitions equally as well planned, if not better, than those of us who went off chasing 1.1's.

Once he started working full time as part of the family forestry business, he became one of the best in the country at his job. He had been sitting in a harvester, or a forwarder since he was old enough to reach the controls, and he had been driving regularly since he was fifteen. He's gifted with his hands, his coordination and his spatial awareness; stuff that you can't really teach.

He has an entrepreneurial mindset, despite having never sat a business class in his life. Despite any financial problems or other obstacles, Kyle made it his goal when he left school to build his family's company up further. He knew that working eighty plus hours a week in his late teens and early twenties could leave him sitting twiddling his thumbs and counting notes by his fortieth birthday.

I learned from Kyle that we can all excel in our own way, and that success is there for the taking if we follow our strengths. At the end of the day, experience really can be the best teacher.

The Stranger smiled as I spoke. "Good man, Clive."

"Absolutely. And Clive isn't the only wise one among us," I replied, as I pointed across the patio to another dear friend and colleague. "That gentleman also." The Stranger looked across the patio.

"He's a DJ, isn't he? What's his name? Jordan, isn't it?"

I nodded in reply, as I rewound the tape of my past to our first few encounters.

If there's one bit of advice that I would give to anyone when it comes to meeting new people, it would be this; don't let the past fool you. You see, when I first met Jordan, I was greeted by a larger than life character, who was extremely well known around Galway as a DJ. My past experiences of being in the company of underage county footballers had scarred me and had convinced me that, given his popularity, Jordan could potentially look down on me.

The reality was quite the opposite. When I first had a conversation with him, sitting in a friend's house after a night shift, it became clear that I was talking to a down-to-earth and genuine gentleman. He was walking proof that our past can mislead us when it comes to the immediate judgement of those that we meet.

One night, in the smoking area of some pub off Eyre Square, he and I discussed his journey as a DJ. He explained to me how he felt very discouraged at first, but then elaborated about how he improved, and how he progressed to playing in nightclubs on a regular basis. I was fascinated. Here was someone making money off something that they loved; here was a man who never gave up.

His talents were fully put into perspective a few minutes later. Whatever pub we were in had a DJ hired for the evening, and I was enjoying the set as a few noughties' throwbacks came and went. Jordan began dissecting the flow of the music in ways that I hadn't even considered. He talked about the poor transitions between songs and broke the art of DJ-ing down for me in less than half an hour, while having my undivided attention in the palm of his hand.

I was inspired.

Jordan had cemented my idea that through belief and persistence, our goals will always be attainable; provided, of course, that we never give up.

I was energised by my recollections. As I sat forward, I couldn't help but smile. "Two absolute geniuses, and not a degree between them. I'll tell you one thing here and now, this life is solely what you make of it, and don't let anyone convince you otherwise."

"I suppose they had your three sacred criteria, the idea, the plan, and the belief."

I nodded quietly and embraced the split second of silence.

"You've sat here for the last couple of hours and you've poured your heart out to me. You've talked about the people whose stories you've listened to with open ears. Do you ever think that you might be a counsellor one day? Put all this 'wisdom' to use?"

"Maybe one day," I replied, after a second of thought. "Although, there is one very wise woman who is certain that I will be. Shortly after Christmas, Ciaran and I met Tiernan's mother, Deniese. She's a student of psychology, and an amazing person to talk to. The clients that she'll encounter in her career really won't know what hit them. She told us about her degree, and essentially everything that she had learned about human thinking. Everything that she said was... was amplified by her personal experiences, and her caring nature. She believes strongly in the power of the universe, and in the idea that... that good things come not just through earning them, but also through belief and positive thinking."

"Fairly similar beliefs to you, then."

"Indeed. Well, she offered us the chance to speak about anything that was playing on our minds; a free counselling session in a sense."

"What card did you play?"

I paused for a moment and pictured the scene once again.

"I had already spilt everything to the two boys, and the extended forming family, but there was one matter that I needed Deniese's opinion on more than any other. I told her about the conflicts and tension between myself and

157

my father... how it all started, and the general progression. As I spoke, she nodded every so often, listening carefully. Then she asked me one simple question... 'Do you want to make peace with him?'... I nodded, and she told me that I had to show this intention, to life, to my father, and to myself. She told me that through my actions, my father would also find the intention to make peace and put our conflicts behind us."

"Ok, I see. A peaceful approach to making peace."

"Exactly. Following this, she then began to talk about a quality that I had overlooked; a quality that many of us have in little doses, but not in abundance. Gratitude. I had always been grateful to a degree. I had been brought up with the mentality of appreciation for my health, my opportunities, and for money. But realistically, like many of us, I had never shown gratitude in abundance... 'I guarantee you,' Deniese said... 'If you start showing gratitude, everything will change.'"

The Stranger took a drag on his cigarette as he listened. "Were you sold on the idea? That gratitude could fix it?"

"I won't lie, I was sceptical. I believed in the power of belief, and I believed in hard work, but I couldn't see how gratitude was going to change anything. Regardless, I was willing to try."

19

Acceptance

"Tell me this," he said, as he removed the cigarette from his mouth, and held it no more than two inches away from his lips. "You hadn't mentioned your father there for a while. How were you and he getting along?"

"We hardly spoke, if I'm honest. I would come home at weekends, work for two days straight and then head back to Galway. On a Sunday morning, he would ask me how the car was, question why I wasn't at mass, tell me who was dead in the vicinity, and then wish me a safe journey once the evening arrived."

The Stranger chuckled.

"Very little had changed then."

"Oh no, my friend, I beg to differ. You see, my abnormal sporting endeavours gave me a name among the regulars in the bar where I worked. My 250-kilo deadlift, or to put into rural units, five hundred-weight, had lowered the jaws of many people, and a sense of respect rippled through the pub. I had bent two of the bars and broken a bench in the local gym whilst being home for Christmas, so my strength was put into perspective. Some questioned why I wasn't full-forward for the senior team, but I pretended not to hear those comments."

"You were causing havoc," he replied, as the cigarette returned to his mouth. "In a sense. As my father sat with a pint, people spoke highly of my efforts to him, even when

159

I wasn't there. My rebellion against the precious Handbook was starting to show a... an undeniable... fruition, I suppose. He, and everyone else, had no choice but to respect a sport, and a way of life, that they had no real regard for."

"And what about this whole... gratitude initiative?"

I paused as my eyes moved towards the cigarette between my fingers.

"It didn't hit me for a couple of months... but then I left home properly. I got a job here through Ciaran's help and planted the flag, you could say. When I got away from the Pyramid and the Chinese Whispers, everything began to make sense."

"It was like a fog had cleared," he replied. "Exactly."

Sunday, April 21st. I worked my last shift at home before leaving. It was five hours behind the bar, and I cannot stress how slowly that day went. When seven pm came, I said good luck to the more pleasant regulars, and literally galloped out the door.

As I got on a bus that evening, I breathed the longest sigh of relief that you could ever imagine. I was out. Free, in a sense.

After the exam pressure had subsided, I settled into the working routine in the place that I now called home. Ciaran and I were in the same boat, willing to work every hour of the day in order to pay rent and put beer on the table.

My perception of the glass had changed; I was now in an environment that I viewed in a completely positive manner, and the flow of thought came with it.

Through my new job, I met an abundance of brilliant, genuine people, many of whom I consider family. Slowly but surely, Deniese's advice sank in.

I was grateful for those around me, grateful for the family, and grateful to be able to enjoy myself in one of the nicest cities in the world.

But then it ran deeper. I was grateful for my exam results, and grateful for the possible opportunities that could come my way.

Then I thought a little further. I was grateful for my sport, grateful for my health that allowed me to compete, and grateful for my coaching and teammates.

I became grateful that I had a roof over my head, food on the table, clothes on my back, and money in my account.

I realised gratitude's power.

You see, gratitude constantly reminds us of all the good that we have. In this frame of mind, envy and comparison struggle to tunnel their way through gratitude's secure walls. Fear and love have their power, but when given a chance, gratitude can completely take over.

And then something else dawned on me. I had found determination through Kyle.

161

I had discovered open-mindedness through Tiernan, Ciaran, Avril, and Olivia. And now I had found gratitude through my conversation with Deniese.

They're character's three pillars; traits that I found in myself through the presence of those around me.

And through gratitude, I began to find acceptance. For everything.

You see, the past is like an archived portfolio that you can look at, but you can't change. The future, however, is like a blank canvas that you can do anything you want with. But not to sound cliché, the present is the most under-rated gift that we have. If your present is a happy and healthy reality, then this portfolio of the past, no matter how difficult it was to create, has been a success. It may be laden with dark recollections, tragedies, and traumas, but it's that exact portfolio that built you into the person that you are today.

As I sat outside the kitchen on a crate, with headphones on and my head resting against the wall behind me, watching cars pass through the drive-thru, acceptance began to play its part with every passing day.

I accepted the fact that depression had greatly impacted me, and that I might never be fully free of its grasp.

I accepted that the Monkey, God rest his soul, had given me trouble, but in his loving memory, I would always be driven to be strong, partly motivated by a peculiar sense of respect in his late honour.

I accepted that as a footballer, I was nothing short of an absolute failure, and that the struggles that were included in that discount package were merely a motivation for me to look elsewhere and find myself.

I accepted that people come and go, that heartbreak has its reasoning, and that our darkest moments are often a prequel to better times that we really couldn't write if we tried.

But most of all, I became extremely grateful for my immediate family; for my mother's endless efforts, and for my father's positive ethics and morals that had found their way to me. I slowly accepted his outlook, and it sank in that he had always meant well in the advice that he passed on, even the parts that I blatantly ignored. His preaching of the Handbook was no fault of his own. Like my maths teacher preaching the delicate importance of 'June', he was obliged to present this default idea that had been instilled in him.

In essence, I began to understand.

"You just had to get away and think clearly for it all to make sense," he said, as he lowered his cigarette.

"Exactly… when I eventually got a chance to come home, or in other words, when I sobered up a bit, my father and I had a conversation. Standing in one of the locals, I explained everything. I stressed that I had meant no disrespect by turning against his beliefs, and that I was merely doing what I felt was right for me. I poured out twenty years' worth of reasoning and logic in the space of about five minutes."

The Stranger's eyes widened as I spoke. "So, what did he say?"

"His hat was off to me. He praised the fact that I had done my own thing, and not blindly followed anyone else. For a few seconds, the Handbook was ripped to shreds. I had proved to him that being 'Normal' was nothing but a mythical restraint." The Stranger paused for a second; he knew that this was a topic of thin ice.

"You must have been relieved to finally put all the tension to rest." "Conversations can change everything, my friend. Believe me... that was one conversation I never thought I'd have."

The Stranger lifted his bottle and held it out in front of him, at head height. "Cheers. To being true to yourself, and to the people who respect it."

I lifted my glass. To say that the mood had changed would be an understatement. The metaphorical jigsaw was coming together.

20

Conversations

After toasting my mental breakthrough, the Stranger placed his bottle by his feet and returned to his cigarette.

"Now…," he said, before pausing for what I can only imagine was a mixture of dramatic effect, and the necessary time he needed to form his intoxicated speech. "Now that you had found acceptance and wisdom through these great people, was it time to start writing?"

"Indeed," I replied. "Because now the clock is ticking."
"What do you mean?"

I couldn't help but smile; he wasn't going to see this coming. So, I downed the last of my vodka, and then turned my attention back to this kind gentleman.

"Through my dear friend Tiernan, I met another incredible individual; another person whose wisdom and intelligence left me speechless and inspired. Deniese's life-long friend, and Tiernan's godmother, is a lady called Miriam. She's the CEO of a digital patient healthcare service company in the pharmaceutical industry called MD Group, which is valued at something around 8 or 9 figures. Myself, Ciaran, & Tiernan visited her in London for a few days, about a month ago. On the first night, we drank in a place called 'The Weir Bar', in Brentford. As we sat around a table, conversing about college life and possible career choices, Tiernan changed the subject and put me severely on the spot. 'Miriam,' he said, 'Conor's thinking about writing a book.' So, she turned to me, intrigued, and eager to hear more. I couldn't help but think, 'Shit, I have to explain my drunken idea to a lady that's worth more money than I could ever fathom.'"

The Stranger's eyes widened.

"Well," he scoffed. "They don't prepare you for that kind of presentation in careers class."

"Exactly. So, I just started talking and hoped for the best. I explained my motives, and the general ideas that I had floating around in my head. After digesting my short spontaneous speech, Miriam paused for a second. 'How long do you think it'll take you to write it?' she asked me. After a moment or two of weighing up how prepared I was, or at least thought I was, I said, 'Give me twelve months.' Miriam nodded, and till the day I die, I'll never forget these words. 'Come back to me on the 13th of June 2020 with a book,' she said. 'And I'll pay for it to be published.'"

"You're not serious, are you?"

"I can't make this up. I was speechless… I struggled to come to terms with what was happening. All I could say was, 'Perfect'. A few minutes later, I found myself standing over a urinal, struggling to breathe, as the reality of the evening hit me."

"Jesus Christ," he replied, equally as shaken as I was in that bathroom in the Weir Bar.

I sat back with my head held high, as I pointed my cigarette in his direction. Drunk Conor was very proud of himself at this point.

"Believe me," I said. "I didn't sleep that night. Goal number three; the most ambitious idea that's ever crossed my mind. And just like that, I had been given the opportunity to make it a reality. June 2018 gave me hope, and June 2019 gave me a method of maybe, just maybe, passing that same hope on to someone else."

The Stranger laughed quietly.

"God. It's mad what a drunk idea can do."

"You're right," I replied, as I took one last look at my glass before setting it on the concrete. "It's funny how these things happen. But if alcohol and the presence of my drunk peers have taught me anything at all, it's that talking can change everything."

I sat forward and focused my eyes on the ground again.

"You see, I've realised that our greatest problems and our biggest ambitions are very similar in a sense. They're here today. They could be gone tomorrow. But whether we choose to act upon them is up to us. If you have an idea, or a problem... or both... talk about them. You never know who's listening. And you never know how your life might change just from saying them out loud."

"You were in London a month ago," he said, as he removed a lighter from his pocket. "So, I assume I've heard everything at this point."

"Yeah, that's pretty much it."

"Well then, do you want to light that, or do you still have that lesson in mind?" I glanced at my cigarette, which was fairly mangled at this point, to say the least. I had an idea in my head, but I had to make sure not to slur my words.

"That there," I said, as I turned to face the Stranger. "That cigarette, for me, represents normality. It represents the idea of playing by everyone else's rules and regulations."

I turned my attention back to the cigarette again, and as I rolled it between my index finger and my thumb, my grip began to slightly tear the white coating.

"You see, I've often found that the opportunity to 'be normal', has always been nearby. I've always had normality somewhere in the palm of my hand. I could have just followed the crowd; I could have set light to this little bullet on several occasions."

I paused, before turning back to the Stranger.

"But I chose not to. Now, I'll be honest, I may have made plenty of mistakes along the way; we all have our regrets, our demons, and our problems. But one thing I will never regret is staying true to myself; following my own path, and chasing my own goals, regardless of anyone else's opinion. That's the greatest investment that I've ever made in myself, and that is the best advice I can give to anyone."

As everyone else left to join the congregation at the front of the house, I stood up and made my way to the table. I stopped for a moment, taking one last look at the wounded cigarette before placing it in the ashtray.

"Right," I said. "I better go; I promised everyone that I would hold an afters. Will you come back with us for one?"

"I better not. Duty calls tomorrow so I better go home and sober up a small bit."

He stood up, and after putting on his jacket, he shook my hand. "Thank you for the chat, my friend. I may have needed it." "Any time, sir, any time."

And with that, he patted me on the shoulder and made his way through the house to join everyone else.

For a second, I stood quietly, observing the empty patio. I couldn't help but laugh at the situation; life really can be strange at times.

I remained fairly silent on the walk home, still coming to terms with the events of the evening. When we arrived in my apartment, the music was resumed, bottles were opened, and the same scene pretty much manifested itself once again in my kitchen.

Exhausted, I crept away from all the excitement and passed out.

When I came out of my self-induced coma a few hours later, the sun was up, and my hangover had set in with little to no mercy. A few of my friends were still in the kitchen, as I made my way to the kettle. Finley, my previously mentioned housemate, was not impressed by the events that had taken place, given that we had kept him awake long before his ten-a.m. training session. But he was understanding, under the circumstances.

He joined me in the corner of the kitchen as I desperately tried to get caffeine into my system.

"In fairness, this morning has been an experience. I've never had a bowl of Cornflakes whilst sitting across from a gram of ketamine before, but sure look, isn't that the way it's gone?"

I threw a teaspoon into the sink. "Yeah, sorry about that."

"Not at all, don't worry," he replied, taking a cereal bar from the cupboard above my head.

"Tell me this," he said. "Have you thought about a setting for the book yet?"

I froze on the spot, as I lifted my head to look out the kitchen window. People were coming and going in the car park, four storeys below us. 'A penny dropping' wouldn't do the moment justice; it was more a case of every pane of glass in my head shattering in one moment. I couldn't help but smile as I turned to Finley, who had stopped chewing in anticipation of my response.

"Do you know what, Finn? I have a great idea."

Lightning Source UK Ltd.
Milton Keynes UK
UKHW021018231120
373921UK00014B/1491